MEDIEVAL LATIN
SCIENTIFIC WRITINGS
IN THE
BARBERINI COLLECTION

MEDIEVAL LATIN
SCIENTIFIC WRITINGS
IN THE
BARBERINI COLLECTION

A Provisional Catalogue

By

THEODORE SILVERSTEIN

THE UNIVERSITY OF CHICAGO PRESS

Library of Congress Catalog Number: 58-5492

THE UNIVERSITY OF CHICAGO PRESS, CHICAGO 37
Cambridge University Press, London, N.W. 1, England
The University of Toronto Press, Toronto 5, Canada

© *1957 by The University of Chicago. Published 1957*
Composed and printed by THE UNIVERSITY OF CHICAGO
PRESS, *Chicago, Illinois, U.S.A.*

FOREWORD

This catalogue of a group of scientific writings in the Vatican Library is the work of one who is neither trained cataloguer nor historian of science but a student of certain aspects of the recovery of learning as they affected literary tradition in the twelfth and thirteenth centuries. Among its many texts only a few may be said to be known to him or to fall within the orbit of his special interests. But the presence in a library where he was working of an important collection so fragmentarily studied was a temptation beyond his strength.

The materials were gathered together in 1953 during a period of some four months, in the midst of other researches and originally without the purpose of forming a catalogue. While lack of time and changing intent are never excuses they are in fact the conditions in which the foundations of the work were laid. Subsequent study at greater leisure in this country has, by raising questions earlier unforeseen, disclosed some shortcomings and inconsistencies (as, for example, among the explicits) which have been adjusted by the use of microfilm. Only a return to the source itself, however, could remove every blemish and this happy journey has not been possible.

It is hoped that all texts have been included which should be. Two, inadvertently omitted, are given simply from various references by Professor Thorndike (see MSS. 270, 306). Others may still be hidden among the thousands of non-scientific items in the collection, arranged as it has been sometimes on rather personal grounds by the elder Pieralisi, but if so they cannot be more than a very few.

v

Upon all these considerations, though care has been taken to produce a catalogue critical for the history of science, the word "provisional" is placed in the title.

This work owes much to the kindness of a number of people: the Fulbright Commission (and the Senator and his colleagues) who made the author's year in Italy possible; the officials of the Vatican Library, including especially its <u>Scrittore</u> Professor A. Campana; and two friends whose authority was entirely unofficial, Dom Anselm Strittmatter of Saint Anselm's Priory, Washington, and Professor Joseph McGrath Bottkol of Mount Holyoke College. Professor Lynn Thorndike has made suggestions which have served to eliminate a number of errors. Finally, the author is obliged to the Division of the Humanities of the University of Chicago and its dean, Napier Wilt, for the financial support necessary for this publication.

Theodore Silverstein

The University of Chicago, 1956

CONTENTS

INTRODUCTION

I. General

That the Barberini collection in the Vatican Library preserves, among its Latin manuscripts, a certain number of medieval scientific texts is not entirely unknown. But the absence of a
printed catalogue and the preoccupation of users of the manuscripts
largely with individual writers or works have left beyond notice how
numerous these texts really are and the significance for the history
of science and for general intellectual history of the collection as a
whole.

From the eighteenth century onward sporadic references to
and uses of the collection have occurred for such items as the physical and astronomical treatises of Blasius of Parma (Affo, Memorie
[1789], II, 119-25), and the musical works of Johannes de Anagnia
and Theodonus de Caprio (see below, MS. 307). In their day and
turn Prince Boncompagni and Moritz Steinschneider borrowed
modestly of its riches, the former for his studies of Andalò di Negro
and Gerard of Cremona (see below, MSS. 156 and 276), the latter in
his classic account of European translations. The eleventh-century
medical miscellany now numbered 160 is, of course, famous. It was
examined by Diels and his co-workers for their great catalogue of
the ancient physicians; from Baehrens and Valentin Rose to Howald
and Sigerist and to Mørland, its texts have been drawn on for editions of Quintus Serenus, Vindicianus, Sextus Placitus and Oribasius.
But here, too, the concern of the editors for the individual writers—
in these instances, moreover, principally for the ancients—has in
effect reduced the body of this manuscript to a series of discrete
fragments, among which the organic significance of the group for
medieval tradition has, as it were, disappeared from view.

The modern growth of interest in medieval science has

1

brought to learned notice a small number of additional items. Thus
Haskins (Med. sci., pp. 208, 274) has pointed, among three of its
codices (178, 179, 156), to some texts of Galen translated by
Burgundio of Pisa, one with additions by Peter of Abano, and to a
translation of Alpetragius by Michael Scot. Saxl has given us an
account of MSS. 76 and 77 (q.v. below), both striking for their
elaborate astrological illustrations. The recently published second
part of Lacombe, Aristoteles latinus, lists MSS. 165 and 305, the
former containing, among other matters, a large part of the Philos-
opher in the Corpus recentius. And that paladin of magic and experimental science Lynn Thorndike has in his various works
brought to light for the first time or anew, besides the Aristotelian
corpus of MS. 165, some thirty or forty separate texts in twenty-
two of the codices.

The fact is, however, that all this hardly scratches the sur-
face of what the Barberini library contains. If we set as a general
limit for what may be included in our scrutiny the boundaries fixed
by Thorndike and Kibre, A catalogue of the incipits of mediaeval
scientific writings in Latin, and add to this a very few texts of such
ancients as Pliny (Nat. hist.), Cicero (Somn. Scip.), Pomponius
Mela and Solinus, we discover upon the simplest examination of
the collection that it includes some ninety-three relevant manuscripts, which together contain approximately 386 Latin texts and
fragments. This without Thorndike and Kibre's occasional latitude
into the vernacular, which, were we to take it, would produce a
considerable number of additional items. The manuscripts range
in time from the tenth through the fifteenth century; the texts
represent, in both what they preserve of the ancients and what is
new, something of the history of Western science before the
twelfth century and a great deal more of it for the subsequent
period to the end of the Middle Ages.

As might be expected of so comprehensive a collection the
body of its texts is of works already familiar to us. But there are
also many otherwise unknown, their incipits and sometimes their
authors unrecorded elsewhere. Even among the familiar works we
are reminded, as Cardinal Ehrle remarks, who negotiated the acquisition of the Barberiniana by the Vatican, that "Jede Handschrift

ist eine Individualität; keine ist der anderen völlig gleich, auch wenn der Inhalt derselbe wäre." Variations in text; marginal gloses; evidence for dating; attributions to translators, adaptors, commentators, glossators and copyists; in some instances illumination and technical figures; occasionally the record of significant possessors; all offer rich detail to the intellectual historian of their times. And when nothing of the sort is true for a particular text, the vagaries of modern critical scholarship may give it special interest from the accident that its manuscript in this collection has been neglected.

This is the case, for example, with the fragment of Pliny's Natural History to be found in MS. 143. Written perhaps in the thirteenth century (or from a thirteenth-century copy?) and originally containing Bks. I-XI entire, this codex seems to have escaped the eye of the current classicist. The collection has four other copies of Pliny, all fifteenth-century; two interesting for their illumination (177, 180), the others for their connection with the humanist Hermolaus Barbarus (162, 163); but of these three are known and the fourth (163), though unknown, is only a continuation of the third (162). Other texts, late Roman and earlier Christian, have also been neglected, such as the Chalcidian Timaeus in MSS. 21 and 22 (xi/xii c.); but this is not surprising since we have as yet for some of the works of which they are copies neither adequate manuscript studies nor critical editions. Pliny, however,— with all the problems that remain—has long been under the editor's scrutiny and is currently appearing anew in the Budé series. Yet here, as also in the editorial tradition from which it descends, there is no evidence that the Barberini codex has been seen.

Among the more strictly mediaeval items the collection's comprehensiveness shows itself in the extent of the subject-matter and the variety of the works within each subject. In medicine the texts run from Hippocrates and Galen, in older Latin versions and new, to the early Salernitans, high Salernitans, post-Salernitans, and from extensive books of several hundred pages to recipes, scribbled in a folio's corner, for cleaning teeth or for getting rid of bugs, fleas and mice. Veterinary medicine, of course, is not omitted. In the mathematical sciences and arts the materials are

especially rich, representing multifariously geometry, time
reckoning, the mathematics of the sphere, perspective, motion
and the curve; the Ptolemaic astronomy and its Arabic and Western
pendants; astrology and astrological prediction; the construction
and use of astrolabe and quadrant; meteorology and weather forecasting; and the theory of music. Aristotle (real and pseudo)
appears, together with his commentators Avicenna, Averroes,
Albertus, Aquinas, Aegidius Romanus, and Petrus de Alvernia.
There are also geographies and books of travel from Aethicus Ister
to Marco Polo and beyond, parts of some of the great encyclopedias,
as well as important summas of general cosmology and cosmogony.
These last include a few poetic works, which display by their nature
something of the impact during the later Middle Ages of science
and learning on imaginative literature.

In all these subjects there are texts which are unknown or
otherwise new.

Among the codices in the field of medicine none turns out,
in a sense, to have newer significance for us than the one which
has been best and longest known in modern times, that is, MS. 160,
to which we have already referred. For this can be seen not only
as carrying down through the Middle Ages until just before the
twelfth century certain books of diseases and cures which survived
the Western empire, but also, when examined beside other similar
manuscripts, as preserving in one of its parts a specific medical
corpus which descends from the tradition of Cassiodorus. It is now
for the first time fully described in the current publication by
Augusto Beccaria, I codici di medicina del periodo presalernitano
(Rome, 1956). Equally important for later, as MS. 160 is for earlier,
medieval medicine are MSS. 178 and 179 (xiv c.). Though both contain substantial groups of Galen's works, neither was known to
Diels and his colleagues. Yet both witness, sometimes rarely, the
medical interests of important figures like Constantinus Afer,
Nicholas of Reggio, Burgundio of Pisa, and Peter of Abano. Among
the other medical manuscripts we expect, and of course we find,
such commonly known writers as Rasis, Mesue, John of Damascus,
Serapion and Al-Kindi, Benedictus Reguardatus de Nursia, Macer,
Platearius, Nicholas Praepositus, Simon of Genoa, Mundinus de

4

Foro Julii (see especially 56, 166, 171, 279, 333). The influential
Arnaldus de Villa Nova, Chaucer's "Arnold of the Newe toun,"
appears (186, 311) in works both genuine and spurious, Latin and
Catalan. The Bolognese Albertus de Zachariis (or Zancariis),
hitherto known from Paris and Leipzig texts, occurs here also
(216), as does the Salernitan Urso (302) in a version varying signif-
icantly from his modern editor's. In veterinary medicine, besides
some scraps on horses and birds of prey and the known but unfortu-
nately sixteenth-century copy of Theodoricus de Cervia (327), the
collection has a version of Laurentius Rusius in Latin (277), untitled,
author unnamed, and without the distinctive dedication by which it
is usually identified. But perhaps the most interesting among the
later texts is a medical work called Liber Guglielminae, which
occupies 317 carefully filled folios of MS. 332. A comprehensive
practical treatise on diseases, with sections on medicines, oils and
unguents, it is, in fact, a copy of the Practica, or Summa conservationis et curationis, of William de Saliceto.

Under the general subject of mathematics and its allied sciences falls so full and varied a group of works that only a very few
select items can be mentioned at present. Geometry is represented
for both ends of the Middle Ages by Euclid in the version attributed
to Boethius and that of Campanus of Novara, evidently revising one
of the two twelfth-century texts of Adelard of Bath (92, 103); time
reckoning by Bede and the computists (e.g. 92, 477); the sphere by
Sacrobosco, among others (260). Even more important are the treatises in physics, including motion and perspective, of Blasius of
Parma, Johannes de Hollandia, Johannes Fontana of Venice, Roger
Bacon, John Peckam and Nicholas of Cusa (348, 350, 357), the last
in a codex written at Brescia ten years after his death (348).

In astronomy Ptolemy's Almagest appears several times in
the usual version from the Arabic by Gerard of Cremona, but in
MS. 173 (xiv c.) an alternate opening chapter and extensive passages
written in the margins disclose a second version from the Arabic.
This is the case, moreover, though considerably less extensively,
with MS. 336 (xv c.). Haskins has noted similar fragments of this
second version in a Wolfenbüttel codex, and of the preface alone in
two Spanish manuscripts as well as in Vatican MS. lat. 2057, all of

the thirteenth century (Med. sci., pp. 106-8). The fact is that the
Vatican copy contains quite fully the other marginal excerpts also,
though their significance has escaped Nogara and their presence
Haskins' discriminating eye; we may suspect the same to be true
of at least one of the Spanish texts, Madrid MS. 10113. Besides all
these, moreover, an exemplar of preface and excerpts, hitherto
also unobserved, may be found in Florence, Bibl. naz. centr., Conv.
soppr., MS. J.IV.20 (xv c.). Probably there are other copies still
hidden on the shelves of libraries in Spain and Italy, if not elsewhere.
Who the translator was of this second Latin version from the Arabic
remains unknown, as does its place of origin, though Haskins' guess
is likely that this was Spain. Whatever its source, however, the evidence now is growing, including that of the two Barberini codices,
of its moderate spread in a tradition of gloses from the early thirteenth to the fifteenth century.

Astrology and astrological prediction, nativities, geomancy,
chiromancy, we may omit from the present account, though the
collection is rich in testimony to man's ingenuity in these mazy
fields. Astrolabes are represented by Hermannus Contractus,
Gerbert and, if the attribution be correct, Hermann of Carinthia
(236, xiv c.), and by Messahala in the version ascribed, though in
somewhat interpolated form, to John of Spain (156, 276). Among
these manuscripts 276 is particularly significant, and for two rea-
sons: it contains among its treatises on the astrolabe an unknown
copy of the treatise on the Quadrant ascribed, among others, to
Robertus Anglicus and John of Montpellier, and it was written by
Johannes de Calamonte Flandrinus, professor at Perugia, who is
known to us for a work on the Alfonsine Tables dated 1467. The
present text not only provides another date (A.D. 1473) in the
career of this fifteenth-century scientist, but also witnesses in its
copious annotation something further of his mathematical learning.

Meteorology and weather forecasting are the subjects of a
small handful of texts and fragments (12, 256, 303) including a copy
of John of Legnano on the comet of 1368 (1952). Besides excerpts
from Isidore and Bede, there are a fragment of Albumasar, a
libellus of Al-Kindi, a compilation of the thirteenth-century
Leopoldus (or Lippoldus), and the pseudepigrapha of Aristotle and

6

Vergil. The pseudo-Aristotle occurs in MSS. 165 and 303, the
second unrecorded by Lacombe, part II. What gives these copies
peculiar interest is that they represent, not the usual version by
Bartholomaeus de Messana, but another, a fragment of which was
detected by Lacombe (I, 409) in Oxford MS. Corp. Chr. 243. The
text in MS. 165 is a similar fragment, but in 303 the variant version
is complete.

Two manuscripts contain the collection's texts in medieval
music, 283 and 307. In the former there is a single work, set between Hugo of St. Victor's Didascalicon and an anonymous cosmology, and entitled in a later hand simply Anonymi Episcopi Tractatus
de Musica. It evidently remains unstudied and unknown. MS. 307,
on the other hand, was known to Coussemaker, who used it for his
texts of Johannes de Anagnia and Theodoricus de Campo. Very recently Casimiri (Note d'archivio per la storia musicale, XIX, 38 ff.)
has examined the codex anew, printed two of its texts and by its
evidence corrected the name of one of the authors from Theodoricus de Campo to Theodonus de Caprio. Even so there remain further items which have continued to elude detection: a fragment,
Capitula de proportionibus (item i), which is anonymous, and another,
Capitulum de octo tonis (item e), ascribed to a Bishop Gregory
(Gregorius praesul), otherwise unidentified.

Aristotle in the Latin tradition is of course variously represented among our manuscripts. He appears chiefly in 165, which
is listed by Lacombe (II, 1162-64) together with MS. 305, containing Avicenna De animalibus. There are further pertinent texts,
however, not so listed. Thus, besides the Liber de significationibus
aquarum et ventorum in MS. 303, the De pomo and the Secreta
secretorum in 52 seem to have escaped the eyes of Lacombe and
his successors. Other works not properly part of this corpus but
reflecting Aristotelian scholarship during the high and late Middle
Ages, are found, among others, in MSS. 309, 676 and 348: commentaries by Thomas Aquinas, Petrus de Alvernia and Aegidius
Romanus chiefly on the Parva naturalia, treatises De vegetabilibus
and De nutrimento by Albertus Magnus, an exposition of the Physics
in the form of quaestiones by Johannes Versor. The popular De
philosophia pauperum, usually ascribed to Albertus Magnus,

7

appears, accompanied by commentary, in MSS. 461 and 462, both
unseen by Grabmann, Geyer and others concerned with the text of
this work.

To the student of general cosmology and cosmogony, especially to one concerned with the effect of the new learning and specula-
tion in these fields on the imaginative literature of the high Middle
Ages, the collection offers several items of special interest. He
will note in passing two copies of Alanus de Insulis, Anticlaudianus
(1771 and 1906), and an unrecorded text, well written and embel-
lished with figures, of the cosmological poet Milo in a manuscript
evidently of French origin (1667). Then he will pause at a long
prose work in MS. 283, anonymous and untitled, but called by a
later rubricator Compendiosus tractatus de philosophia et eius
secretis. In it he will find a summary account of the natural uni-
verse, from God and the Trinity, angels, man and the elements, to
commixtiones, congelati and sapores. If he seeks to define its time
and character he will be reminded in part of several anonymous
treatises on the elements described by Haskins (Med. sci., pp. 93-
95) as of, or serving as a bridge to, the thirteenth century. It gives
a quotation from Aristotle, De animalibus, which, if genuinely first-
hand, would place the work in the time of Michael Scot or after. But
its main scientific sources—Constantinus Afer, Johannitius,
Hippocrates De humana natura—are those of the Salernitan line in
the twelfth century, and its account of the elements makes a specific attack on this line; pravi Salernitani, as its author calls them.

Not less interesting for the same subject are the contents of
MS. 2089, the poetical works of Gregory de Monte Sacro, a writer
completely unknown to the historians of medieval literature. The
manuscript, written in the thirteenth century and perhaps after the
author's death, evidently collects all that remained of his labors,
including some incomplete sequences in honor of various saints.
The chief piece, however, is a long poem in Latin hexameters entitled Peri ton Antropon theopiisis, accompanied by an elaborate
commentary on the text, the whole occupying 131 folios. A mystical
account of the first seven days, it belongs in that hexaemeral tradition whose renaissance in the twelfth and thirteenth centuries
helped to produce the philosophic poetry of Bernardus Silvestris,

Alanus de Insulis, Milo, Alexander Neckam and others, and left its
mark on the vernacular literature especially of France and England.
In this tradition Gregory de Monte Sacro must now be reckoned
especially significant, since he adds to what has hitherto seemed an
almost exclusively Anglo-French preoccupation, the evidence (not
without further testimony from elsewhere) of a similar interest
arising in Italy.

Nor have we yet exhausted the collection's riches. For there
are texts of Gervase of Tilbury (2611) and the encyclopedist Thomas
of Cantimpré (666). There are poems on "scientific" subjects, not
recorded elsewhere, by such Italian writers as Bishop Baptista
Pallavicini and Hieronymus Guarinus (42). And the well-known
Venetian churchman, Dominicus de Dominicis, bishop of Torcello
and of Brescia, appears in several rare and evidently unprinted
treatises, one on the subject of the interior senses (1227).

Finally, among what may be called the accidental aspects of
the texts—the date and place of an explicit, a scribe's name, and,
even more accidentally, the names and dates of possessors, the
place and cost of acquisition or the statement of a bequest—are
numerous records of varying interest and significance. Not every
scribe, to be sure, turns out to be a professor of science like
Johannes de Calamonte Flandrinus; nor every possessor to be a
distinguished collector like Carolus Strozze; nor every owner's
signature to be that of Luca Holstenius, geographer, librarian to
the seventeenth-century Barberini, scholar extraordinary, and
friend of the young John Milton. But these are there among the
others and for the moment they will do.

II. Technical

Before describing the considerations which form the present
Catalogue it may not be superfluous to recall the chief consideration,
namely, that the Catalogue is addressed primarily to the historian
of science and of ideas, that therefore it necessarily differs in some
respects from the more general manuscript catalogue. The differ-
ence shows itself largely in the selection and treatment of problems,
which center rather on matters of relevant content than on the
paleographical, ornamental or other physical aspects of the manu-

scripts themselves. Such aspects are of course not neglected (indeed they have sometimes been considered extensively), but they have been seen by the cataloguer as a secondary concern and are not therefore always treated with uniform attention.

The principles and practices which have been followed are these:

A. Limits

The Catalogue is confined strictly to Latin texts and to manuscripts written not later than the fifteenth century. This at once eliminates such vernacular works classified in the Latin section of the Barberini library as Aldobrandino's Libro della fisica, a poema on the sphere by Gregorio Dati, an anonymous Libro d'aritmetica e geometria (3907, 3956, 3957, and 4048, all xv c.), and Ristoro d'Arezzo's Composizione del mondo (4110, xiii c.), as well as the manuscripts in which they occur. Books and scraps of mathematics, medicine and veterinary medicine in French, Italian, Catalan will be found throughout the Catalogue in the General Account of manuscripts recorded primarily for their Latin works. A very few besides these, chiefly recipes, appear in the main listings since they are interwoven with the Latin and belong with them.

The limit of time poses some problems. It has no virtue in itself, but plainly most of the manuscripts written after the fifteenth century belong to another history. There are, however, several of the sixteenth century or later which contain medieval works or adaptations of them. MS. 212, for example, is a book of chiromancy a me Joanne Andrea Cruciano expletus and said to be based on a translation from the Arabic by John of Spain (whichever John this may be); 273 and 334 have various alchemical works, including Arnaldi Lucidarium metris compositum (273, fols. 165 ff.) and the Morienus ascribed to Robert of Chester (334, fols. 1-26^V); 327 is a copy of the Mulomedicina of Theodoricus de Cervia; and 904 preserves (fols. 229^V-30), among a group of non-scientific writings, Antonius Arquatus, Pronosticum eversionis Europae circa annum 1507. But most of these manuscripts are known, certainly all of the works. At the risk of seeming finicky the Catalogue has kept its limit and omitted them except for their mention here.

10

B. Method of Listing Manuscripts and Texts

Each manuscript is described in three parts: its Number, its Contents and a General Account of its character and present condition.

Number: the present designation of the manuscript in the Vatican Library; and, within parentheses, its previous Barberini number, its reference in Pieralisi's Inventarium and any earlier library numbers of whatever source which it preserves (= n.a.).

Contents: a listing of its Latin scientific texts only. Where there are other works in it as well, these are relegated to the General Account following the Contents; and a prefatory statement warns the reader that this has been done. As for the scientific texts themselves, they are also listed in three parts: (1) Title— given normally as found in the manuscript, even when it appears as for only part of the text, provided always that there is no ambiguity as to what work is intended. Titles are supplied from elsewhere for unnamed works or fragments, when identified, and, when not, are made up by the present cataloguer from the nature of the contents. Modifications of the manuscript title are ordinarily limited to the designation of author, translator or adaptor, or to indicate that the book is fragmentary or expanded. All such modifications are made plain by the use of claw-hammer brackets. (2) Incipit and Explicit—usually brief and for the beginning and end of the text as a whole. Sometimes, however, as with a peculiar version, space is taken to include words that are symptoms of the peculiarity; prefatory matter may be specially marked out; and in the case of otherwise unknown works the incipits (and occasionally explicits) of their various parts may be given as indications of contents or as aids to the discovery of them elsewhere. "Explicit" usually means the last words of a text together with scribal colophon or end-rubric, when there is one, the latter being regularly recorded since often, as may be expected, it contains data of importance for the book's origin and history, or for its influence. The general exception to this practice will be found among works which are primarily tables or figures having brief explanatory passages; in these instances only an incipit (sometimes an explicit) is ordinarily set down. It should be added that among the inconsist-

11

encies remaining in the Catalogue (as referred to above in the Foreword) is the absence, though infrequently, of a text-ending where it ought to be. (3) Notes — in square brackets following each separate item, they vary considerably in length and import according as the work itself, its problems, the general state of information about it, and the cataloguer's knowledge have determined. But some features are fairly constant, e.g. reference where possible to a printed edition, old or new, and notice of modern citations or uses of the item in question. Throughout incipits have been checked against Thorndike and Kibre, A catalogue of incipits of mediaeval scientific writings in Latin (and its Supplements) and all instances are remarked of their non-appearance in that Catalogue, as well as those of its listings which depend specifically on a Barberini text. Some of the incipits are, to be sure, of excerpts from larger works, which Thorndike and Kibre do not set out to record; but many such excerpts have achieved a virtually separate existence, and even in the case of certain fragments to state that they are "not in Thorndike and Kibre" may have the value of eliminating one step in the further search for their texts. It will be obvious that much of what is peculiarly valuable about the Catalogue resides in these Notes, since they distill the results of the cataloguer's attempt to identify texts and distinguish versions, to indicate the nature of their subject-matter, discover their sources and record the currently significant scholarship bearing upon them.

General Account: a description of the character of the manuscript containing the usual elements found in catalogues. Measurements, when given, are not for leaves but columns since, among codices so miscellaneous in nature and provenience, variation in the column's dimensions and number of lines is sometimes a simpler clue than any other to a new hand or a changed circumstance of the writing. To the description of the manuscript is added, as conditions warrant, information on its present state: losses or additions of leaves; additions, contemporary or later, of texts, titles, gloses; signatures and statements of possessors; occasionally the binding. If there are among the texts non-scientific writings or scientific writings in a vernacular tongue, this, as already noted, is the section where they are recorded.

C. Abbreviations

The abbreviated titles used in the Catalogue will, it is hoped, be understood without special explanation. Those which appear most frequently are listed here:

Beiträge. Beiträge zur Geschichte der Philosophie und Theologie des Mittelalters, ed. Baeumker, von Hertling, Grabmann, et al. (Münster in W.). Reference by Band, Heft and page.

Bibl. math. Bibliotheca mathematica: Zeitschrift für Geschichte der mathematischen Wissenschaften, ed. G. Eneström (Leipzig and Berlin). Reference by Folge, Band and page.

Boncompagni, Bullettino. Bullettino di bibliografia e di storia delle scienze matematiche e fisiche: Vols. I-XX (Rome, 1868-87).

Carmody, Ar. astron. F. J. Carmody, Arabic astronomical and astrological sciences in Latin translation: A critical bibliography (Univ. of California Press, 1956). Reference by author and item numbers.

Coussemaker, Script. mus. med. aev. E. de Coussemaker, Scriptorum de musica medii aevi novam seriem a Gerbertina alteram collegit nuncque primum edidit (Paris, 1864): 4 Vols.

Diels. H. Diels, "Die Handschriften der antiken Ärzte," Abhandlungen der K. Preuss. Akad. der Wissenschaften, Philos.-hist. Klasse: Teil I, 1905, Abh. 3; Teil II, 1906, Abh. 1; Teil III, 1907, Abh. 4. Reference by Teil and page.

Gerbert, Script. eccles. de musica. M. Gerbert, Scriptores ecclesiastici de musica sacra potissimum ex variis Italiae, Galliae & Germaniae codicibus manuscriptis collecti et nunc primum publica luce donati (Typis San-Blasianis, 1784): 3 Vols.

Giacosa, Mag. salern. Pietro Giacosa, Magistri salernitani nondum editi (Torino, 1901).

Haskins, Med. sci. C. H. Haskins, Studies in the history of mediaeval science (Cambridge, Mass., 2nd ed., 1927).

Hauréau, Schedario. Unpublished list of miscellaneous incipits, Manuscript Reading Room of the Vatican Library.

Isis, XIII. Lynn Thorndike, "Vatican Latin manuscripts in the history of science and medicine," Isis, XIII (1929-30), 53-102.

Lacombe. G. Lacombe et al., Aristoteles latinus (Corpus philosophorum medii aevi academiarum consociatarum auspiciis et consilio editum, Union Académique Internationale): Pars I (Roma, 1939); Pars II (Cambridge, Eng., 1955).

Pieralisi. Unpublished inventory of the Latin Barberiniani, Manuscript Reading Room of the Vatican Library.

Steinschneider, Sitzungsber. M. Steinschneider, "Die europäischen Übersetzungen aus dem Arabischen bis Mitte des 17. Jahrhunderts," Sitzungsberichte der K. Akad. der Wissenschaften in Wien, Philos.-hist. Klasse: Vol. CXLIX (1905); Vol. CLI (1906).

Thorndike. Lynn Thorndike, History of magic and experimental science: Vols. I-II (New York, 1923); Vols. III-IV (1934).

Thorndike and Kibre. Lynn Thorndike and Pearl Kibre, A catalogue of incipits of mediaeval scientific writings in Latin (Mediaeval Academy Publ. No. 29, Cambridge, Mass., 1937). The phrase "Not in Thorndike and Kibre" refers to this volume and all its supplements:

Suppl. I. "Additional incipits of mediaeval scientific writings in Latin," Speculum, XIV (1939), 93-105.

Suppl. II. "More incipits," Speculum, XVII (1942), 342-66.

Suppl. III. "Further incipits," Speculum, XXVI (1951), 673-95.

CATALOGUE

10 (VIII. 10: Pieralisi I, 11).

Marciani Minei Felicis Capelle De Nvpciis Mercvrii et Philologye: Liber primus incipit.

<u>Inc.</u>: <T>V quem psallentem . . . fol. 1

<u>Expl.</u>: Faueantque muse et chelis Latoia. MARCIANI MINEI FELICIS CAPELLE DE NVPCIIS MERCVRII ET PHILOLOGYE LIBER SECVNDVS EXPLICIT. fol. 53^V

[Bks. i and ii complete. Ms. not in eds. Eyssenhardt (1866) or Dick (1925) and their refs.; nor in Schanz-Hosius-Krüger, VIII. 4, 2 (1920), 170, and its refs. Cf. below, <u>MS. 130.</u> On fol. 1, marg., glose begins <u>Iste Marcianus afer fuit genere ciuis atheryensis Romanus dignitate</u> . . .]

xiv c., parchment, 53 fols., single cols. 11.5 x 5.5 cms., 18 lines but varying. Written in single hand. Gloses, marginal and interlinear, throughout in another contemporary hand. Rubr. in red.

12 (VIII. 12: Pieralisi I, 13-15; n.a. 1915).

A miscellany of texts and fragments, of which the following works are relevant to the present collection:

<u>a)</u> Palladii rutilii tauri emiliani uiri illustris opus agriculture incipit.

<u>Inc.</u>: Pars est prima prudencie ipsam cui precep-
turus . . . fol. 1

<u>Expl.</u>: Palladii . . . opus de agricultura explicit. fol. 87^V

[Ms. not in ed. Schmitt (1898). Cf. Schanz, <u>Gesch. d. röm. Litt.</u>, IV. 1, 173.]

<u>b)</u> <Libellus de morbis iumentorum.>

<u>Inc.</u>: Plerumque iumenta morbos concipiunt ex lassitu-
dine et estu. non numquam ex frigore . . . fol. 88

15

Expl.: ut glegma congestum possit aboleri.   fol. 94

[Not in Thorndike and Kibre.]

<u>c</u>) De Auibus rapacibus marscallia incipit.

Inc.: Ad ancipitris tesquam. Accipe de felle

uerris . . .   fol. 94^V

Expl.: et carnem eius intinge ut. et sanabit ut.   fol. 95

[The French connection of this fragment, suggested
by other items in the codex, is also evident from the
word tesqa; for which see G. Tilander, <u>Glanures lexi-</u>
<u>cographiques</u> (Lund, 1932), <u>s.v. tegge, tesquer.</u> Pres-
ent ms. not in, e.g., Werth, in <u>Zeitschr. f. röm. Philol.</u>,
XII (1888), 146 ff., 381 ff., and XIII (1889), 1 ff., Bieder-
mann, the same, XXI, 529-40; or Tilander. Not in
Thorndike and Kibre.]

<u>d</u>) Incipit de architectura ualde utili sciencia de libris anti-

quorum qui hoc scripserit non paruo labore excerpta.

Inc.: Multa oracione de artis archi<tec>torie peri-

cia . . .   fol. 98

Expl.: dabis unicuique $\bar{x}$. et omni articulo $\bar{c}$. Explicit.   fol. 110^V

[Not in Thorndike and Kibre.]

<u>e</u>) <Pseudo-> Aristotiles. <De tempestatum presagiis.>

Inc.: De tempestatum presagiis tractaturi a Sole capie-

mus exordia. Purus oriens . . .   fol. 110^V

Expl.(mutil.): Omnis igitur urbs $\bar{q}$ om[?]   fol. 115

[Cf. Pliny, <u>Nat. hist.</u>, XVIII, 341-42 (ed. Jan-Mayhoff,
III, 238); and Oxford <u>MS. Digby 28</u> (see Hellmann,
<u>Beiträge z. Gesch. d. Meteorol.</u>, II, 194).]

<u>f</u>) <Pseudo-> Virgilius de tempestatum presagiis.

Inc.: In uernali tempore et autumnali tempestates

maxime concitantur . . .   fol. 115^V

Expl.: fugiens in uado ludit.   fol. 116

[On basis for ascribing to Vergil a work about
weather forecasting, see <u>Georg.</u>, I, 311 ff.; Pliny,
<u>Nat. hist.</u>, XVIII, 340 (ed. Jan-Mayhoff, III, 237);
and Isidore, <u>De nat. rer.</u>, cap. 38, § 4 (PL,
LXXXIII, 1010), which attributes to the poet a
passage beginning <u>Si sol in ortu suo maculosus</u> . . .
(see next item below). Not in Hellmann, II, esp.
194; nor Thorndike and Kibre.]

16

g) Beda de signis tempestatum et serenitatis

Inc.: Sol in ortu suo maculosus . . .　　　　　fol. 116

Expl.: discurse celum aperiunt.　　　　　　　fol. 116

　　[Bede, De natura rerum, cap. 36 (PL, XC, 254-55).
　　Not in Thorndike and Kibre.]

h) <Quaestiones de experimentis variis.>

Inc.: Queritur de carne elixata cur per decoccione
remolliatur . . .　　　　　　　　　　　　　fol. 116^V

Expl.: matizabis de auri pigmento.　　　　　fol. 118

　　[Not in Thorndike and Kibre.]

i) <Capitulum de propriis nominibus arborum.>

Inc.: Palma est arbor insignis . . .　　　　　fol. 121

Expl.: medicari potius uideatur quam [?] alere.　fol. 123^V

　　[Drawn from Isidore, Etym., XVII. vii. 1-6
　　(ed. Lindsay). Not in Thorndike and Kibre.]

j) <Collectus formularum colorum latine et gallice
scriptarum.>

Inc. pr.: Ad cristallum conplimendum in figura . . .　fol. 124

Expl. pr.: siccum cooperie de caule.　　　　　fol. 125^V

Inc. alt.: Chescune colur mulez . . .　　　　　fol. 126

Expl. alt.: uostrer orne metez pag.　　　　　fol. 128

Inc. tert.: De distemperandis coloribus. ad scriben-
dum uel illuminandum . . .　　　　　　　　fol. 128

Expl. tert.: Sequitur de auro. Quere in sexte folio
quaterni sequentis et inuenies.　　　　　　fol. 128

　　[Incipits not in Thorndike and Kibre.]

k) <Fragmentum De virtutibus arborum.>

Inc.: In arboribus quedam naturaliter stiptice . . .　fol. 130

Expl. (mutil.): pediculi et sic auferes eos　　　fol. 132^V

　　[Not in Thorndike and Kibre.]

l) <Formula ad inveniendum si locus sit bonus an malus.>

Inc.: Quom scire possis si locus sit bonus an malus.
fossam fode in terram et pone intus ligna iuncta ad
modum crucis . . .　　　　　　　　　　　　fol. 133

17

[Not in Thorndike and Kibre.]

m) <Formulae miscellaneae medicinarum.>

Inc.: Zucara rosata sic fit . . .   fol. 133^V

Expl.: Ydromel sic fit . . . Pusca sic fit . . . et tres
uini.   fol. 134

[Not in Thorndike and Kibre.]

n) <Aliae formulae colorum.>

Inc.: In primis fac elexiuam . . .   fol. 135

Expl.: appina [?] ei acetum.   fol. 136

[Not in Thorndike and Kibre.]

o) <Aliae formulae colorum latine et gallice scriptae.>

Inc.: Ardez une pere que lem apele sperston . . .   fol. 137

Expl. (mutil.): aqua uiridi misceatur. quare et
uirorem perdit   fol. 138^V

[Not in Thorndike and Kibre.]

p) <Fragmenta formularum medicinarum.>

Inc.: <A>d usum medicine habent colligi flores.
semina . . .   fol. 139

Expl. (mutil.): argentum uinum recedat. et in
subtilissi   fol. 140^V

[Not in Thorndike and Kibre.]

q) <Continuatio formularum latine et gallice scriptarum.>   fols. 141-
                                                             41^V

Expl.: <c>omprez le od gume.   fol. 141^V

[Cf. above, item o.]

xiv c., parchment, 145 fols. (numbered 1-144, with an unnumbered
leaf marked 124^a in modern pencil). A complicated collection in
many hands which has suffered serious injury; repaired and re-
bound in 1826. For the items listed above there are at least three
hands: (1) items a, b, c, and n; (2) items d-m; and (3) items o-q.
In addition there are texts, notes, and fragments by various others:
Fols. 95^V-96, an anonymous sermon. Fols. 118-20^V, Marscaucis
de cheuaus. Fols. 96^V-97^V, miscellaneous recipes, including a
French fragment De herbe Betise. Fols. 95, 121, 129^V, 139^V-40,

18

142-43^V, various scraps, recipes, notes, some in margins. Rubr. in red, blue, purple, green.

21 (VIII. 21: Pieralisi I, 27; n.a. 1399).

a) <Platonis Timaeus interprete Chalcidio.>

Inc. prol. Chalcidii: Socrates in exhortationibus
suis uirtutem laudans . . .   fol. 1

Expl. text. Platonis: et ex leui admonitione
perspicuo. FINIT.   fol. 33

[See ed. Wrobel (Leipzig, 1876), pp. 3-69; for the
reading Socrates in the incipit, p. 3, n. 1. Present
ms. not in Schanz, Gesch. d. röm. Litt., VIII. 4, 1
(1904), 127, or its refs.; nor in Tamilia, Stud. ital.
di filol. class., VIII (1900), 79-80. Cf. below, MS. 22.]

b) <Platonis Timaeus commentatore Chalcidio.>

Inc.: Timeus platonis et a ueteribus difficilis
habitus . . .   fol. 34

Expl.: sermo ad perfectionem institutionis ingenue.
CALCIDIVS IN TIMEO EXPLICIT.   fol. 110^V

[Various figures throughout illustrating text of the
commentary. See ed. Wrobel, pp. 69-379. Cf. below,
MS. 22.]

xi/xii c., parchment, 110 fols. Originally two separate mss.: (1)
Fols. 1-33, single cols. 11.8 x 6.3 cms., 20 lines. Written in single
hand. Some gloses, marginal and interlinear, in various hands,
contemporary and later. Fol. 33^V, originally blank, now has gloses.
Rubr. initials bks. I and II, and incipit bk. II. (2) Fols. 34-110,
single cols., written in single hand. Marginal notes and gloses in
various hands, one later in red ink. This part has older fol. numbering in ink, 1-77, but both parts together are now renumbered in
pencil, 1-110. Ownership note on fol. 34, top: Iste liber est conu-
entus fratrum minorum de Senis . . .

22 (VIII. 22: Pieralisi I, 28; n.a. 1400).

Chalcidius in Timaeum <cum translatione eiusdem textus>
Platonis. Incipit Prologus in Timevm Platonis de Greco
in Latinvm petente Iosio a Calcidio viro claro translatvm.
et miro ingenio commentatvm et elucidatvm.

19

Inc. prol. Chalcidii: Iosio suo Calcidius ; Socrates senex
in exhortationibus suis uirtutem laudans . . .   fol. 1^V

Inc. text. Platonis: VNVS. DVO. TRES . . .   fol. 1^V

Inc. pars prima comm.: Timeus Platonis et a
ueteribus difficilis habitus . . .   fol. 7^V

Inc. pars secunda text.: Et iam fere cuncta . . .   fol. 33

Inc. pars secunda comm.: Mvndi totius perfectionem . . .   fol. 38

Expl. comm.: que consentaneos motus animae
celestibus tramitibus dirigebant.   fol. 52

[Contains the Chalcidian commentary, divided into
Prologue and two parts (at sec. 119; ed. Wrobel,
p. 184); and the text, also divided in two (at sec. 39E;
ed. Wrobel, p. 39, l. 15), each part being placed before
the corresponding section of the commentary. Commentary ends, incomplete, at opening of sec. 208 (ed.
Wrobel, p. 247, l. 9). Present ms. not in Tamilia nor
Schanz: cf. MS. 21 above. For significance of the
forms of reference to Chalcidius and Osius in the
title and prologue see Tamilia, p. 80.]

xi c., parchment, 52 fols., double cols. 14.4 x 4.8 cms., 40 lines.
Written in single hand. Date of a later owner on fol. 1: anno domini
m^{o}cc^{o}lx^o.

32 (VIII. 32: Pieralisi I, 42-44; n.a. 2589).

A miscellany of excerpts chiefly from ancient Latin and
Church writers, of which one is relevant to the present catalogue:

<M. Tulli Ciceronis Somnium Scipionis.>
Inc.: CVm affricam venissem a mallio consule . . .   fol. 9
Expl.: Ille discessit ego sompno sollicitus sum.
Deo gratias. Amen.   fol. 12^V

xv c., parchment, 18 fols. Written, double cols. varying sizes, in
four or more hands. Contents and hands thus: (1) Fols. 1-6, Sallust,
De bello Cat. (2) Fols. 6-8, excerpts from Cicero, De officiis, and
rubr. to Sallust, De bello Cat. and Jugurtha. (3) Fol. 8^V, excerpts
from anon. Christian, De prudentia, fato, fortuna et casu. (4) Fols.
9-18^V, Cicero, Somn. Scip.; excerpts from Seneca, De ira, Augustine, De civ. Dei iv. 3, Thomas de Perusia, Sermo Maiores nostri,

note on life of Thomas de Perusia, Responsio S^r. Colutii Salutati
ad eundem Thomam super quadam epistola transmissa, and ex -
cerpts from Cicero's Rhetorica vetera. On fol. 8 the hand for that
section is identified: Antonius de Manfredis de firmo potestas
ciuitatis fulginei manu propria scripsit.

42 (VIII. 42: Pieralisi I, 56-62; n.a. 2127).

A miscellany of the lives of emperors, philosophers, famous
women, etc., among which four items are of present interest:

a) L. COELI LACTANTII FIRMIANI DE OPIFICIO DEI
   SEV HOMINIS FORMATIONE.
   Inc.: QVAM minime sim quietus etiam in summis . . . fol. 2
   Expl.: liberatos ad iter celeste direxerit. FINIS.
      LVDOVICVS Sandeus scripsit anno a Christi
      natiuitate M^o ccc^o lxvi^o: AEtatis uero eius anno
      xx^o: augusto xiii^o.   fol. 41^V

   [Capitula listed on fols. 42-42^V. Present ms. not
   in ed. Brandt-Laubmann or its refs.: Corp. script.
   eccles. lat., XIX, xiii ff.; and XXVII, vii ff. Incipit
   not in Thorndike and Kibre. Cf. below, MS. 677, item a.]

b) Columella in prooemio libri primi de re rustica.
   Inc.: Omnes enim (sicut M. Varro iam tempori-
      bus . . .) . . .   fol. 284
   Expl.: ut nihil mors mutatura uideatur / Et cetera.   fol. 284

   [A fragment of preface to bk. I, beginning in § 15
   and ending in § 17: see, e.g., ed. Lundström (Coll.
   script. vet. Upsal.), II, 9.]

c) Baptistę Marchionis Palauicini Episcopi Regiensis
   carmen de ficu.
   Inc.: Alma parens hominum tellus rerumque
      creatrix . . .   fol. 286
   Expl.: Tu tantum interea superis hanc desine
      curam. Τελος.   fol. 289

   [By the bishop of Reggio in Lombardia. Not listed
   in accounts of eds. Treviso, 1494, and Vienna, 1511;
   nor by Fabricius, Bibl. lat. med. et inf. aet. (ed.
   1858), I, 159; Trithemius; Gesner; etc. Not in
   Thorndike and Kibre.]

d) Hieronymus Guarinus ad quendam Guizardum de ventis.

    Inc.: Perlege queso rudis monumenta . . .   fol. 322^V

    Expl.: cognoscere ad vnguem. hieronymi que tui

    poteris meminisse Guizarde.   fol. 322^V

    [There follows a figure showing the names and
    location of the winds. Incipit not in Thorndike
    and Kibre.]

xv c., paper, 348 fols., including 2 blank leaves originally unnumbered but now included in the modern renumbering of the folios,
which present description follows. Original numbering was: a,
fols. 1-40^V; b, fol. 282; c, fols. 284-87; d, 320^V. Written in 1466 by
Ludovicus Sandeus (as on fol. 41^V), for whom see Quadrio, Indice
universale, II, 209, and VII, 99.

45 (VIII. 45: Pieralisi I, 69; n.a. 816).

    <Aethici Istris Cosmographia.> Incipit liber Ethicorum
    translatus philosofico edito oraculo Ieronimo presbytero
    dilatum ex cosmographia id est mundi scriptura edicio
    ethici philosophi cosmographi.

    Inc.: philosophorum scedulas sagaci inuestigans

    indagatione mihi laborem . . .   fol. 1

    Expl.: quos nos indaganter inuestigauimus. Amen.   fol. 49

    [Ms. not listed in M. D'Avezac, Ethicus (Paris,
    1852), esp. pp. 9-13; nor in ed. Wuttke (2nd ed.,
    Leipzig, 1854), esp. pp. cxvii-cxxxiii. Cf. Manitius,
    Gesch. lat. Lit. d. M.A., I, 234.]

xv c., paper, 49 fols., single cols. Written in single hand. Modern
rebinding (1827).

52 (VIII. 52: Pieralisi I, 77-78; n.a. 2725 and C. 17).

A miscellany of four texts, of which three are on scientific
    subjects:

a) <Pseudo-Aristotelis Liber de secretis secretorum
    translatus per Philippum Tripolitanum.>
    Inc.: Domino suo excellentissimo et cultu religionis
    Christiane . . .   fol. 1
    Expl.: toti orbi terrarum dictus Monarchia in septen-
    trione. Explicit liber aristotelis qui intitulatus est

de secretis sectorum [sic] ac regimine domino-
rum.   fol. 19

[See Lacombe, pp. 93 and 195 and nn.; and Grabmann,
Forschungen, p. 250. Ms. not listed in Foerster,
Zentralblatt, VI (1889), 9 esp.; ed. Foerster, Scrip-
tores physiog., II, 182 ff. (cf. I, clxxviii ff.); nor
Lacombe, II, 1162-64.]

b) <Pseudo-Aristotelis Libellus de pomo translatus per
    Manfredum regem Siciliae.>

Inc. prol.: Cvm homo creaturarum dignissima similitudo sit . . .   fol. 19^V

Inc. text.: Cvm clausa esset uia veritatis sapi-
enti . . .   fol. 19^V

Expl.: sicut dignum est animam hominis directi
et perfecti sicut tu es. Explicit liber aristotelis
de pomo.   fol. 22

[See Lacombe, pp. 94 and 196 and nn.; and Grabmann,
Forschungen, pp. 249 f. Cf. below, MS. 165, item s. Ms.
not in Lacombe, II, 1162-64.]

c) <Anonymi Medicamenta contra muscas, pulices, cimices,
    mures, etc.>

Inc.: Contra muscas. Cum eleboro albo puluerizato . . .
Contra pulices. Adipes yrcini . . . Contra Cimices.
detoquantur lupatum [?] uehementer . . . Contra
formicas. pone sulfur . . .   fol. 24

Expl.: Idem facit si circumsculpis dentes cum radice
pastinace.   fol. 24^V

[Incipit not listed in Thorndike and Kibre.]

xiv c., parchment, 24 fols., single cols. 17.8 x 10.8 cms., 42-44
lines. Written in single hand. Contains (fols. 22-24), in addition to
items a-c above, a work entitled Translatio abbreviata fratris
Petri Episcopi Cartaginensis de speculatione antecer [?] in regi-
tiua domus . . . Some marginal gloses. Rubr. in red, blue, green,
purple, and gold. On inside front cover a stamp: Governo di Roma.
On verso of fly leaf a note in recent hand: tornato alla libreria
dopo di essere stato al Governo di Roma.

23

55 (VIII. 55: Pieralisi I, 82-83; n.a. 861).

A miscellany, of which two items are relevant:

a) Cicero De somnio Scipionis.

Inc.: <C>VM in affricam uenissem . . .   fol. 40

Expl.: Ille discessit ego sompno solutus sum.   fol. 47

b) <Vibii Sequestris Index sive catalogus fluminum,
     lacuum, fontium, montium.>

Inc.: QVanto ingenio ac studio fili carissime apud
     plerosque poetas fluminum . . .   fol. 48

Expl.: Volsci italici.   fol. 58^V

> [Cf., e.g., ed. Riese, <u>Geogr. lat. min.</u> (1878), pp. 145-
> 58; and Schanz-Hosius-Krüger, VIII. 4, 2 (1920), 122.]

xv c., parchment, 58 fols., single cols. 14.5 x 9 cms., 23 lines,
except fols. 40-47 which are 14 x 8.5 cms., 21 lines. Written in at
least three similar hands, as follows: (1) fols. 1-11^V, Rufus Sextus,
<u>Rer. gest. pop. rom. liber</u>; (2) fols. 14-47, Cicero, <u>De amic</u>. and
<u>Somn. Scip.</u>; and (3) fols. 48-58^V, Vibius Sequester. Completion of
Rufus Sextus dated, fol. 11: <u>Explicit Feliciter die xv. mensis octo-
bris M cccc xxxviii</u>. Initials rubr. in blue, red and gold.

56 (VIII. 56: Pieralisi I, 84-85; n.a. 2130 and 773).

A miscellany of five items, of which two are scientific
     writings in Latin:

a) <Macri Floridi Carmen de viribus herbarum.>

Inc.: Incipit macer. Herbarum quasdam dicturus
     carmine . . .   fol. 23

Expl.: Heraclea herba est mirabilis virtutis . . .
     alii pari<e> talis alii ferraria.   fol. 39^V

> [Varies in part from Macer, ed. L. Choulant
> (Leipzig, 1832), pp. 28-140. See also Choulant,
> <u>Handbuch</u> (1841), I, 233-44; and Thorndike, I,
> 612-15 and notes. Cf. below, <u>MS. 171</u>, item <u>f</u>.]

b) <Tractatus anonymi de chyromantia.>

Inc.: Hanc scientiam iudicare per manus lineas
     naturales . . .   fol. 43

Expl.: et dicitur cyromancia compilata et agregata
     per magistrum.   fol. 50

[There follows, fol. 50^V, a diagram of a hand,
showing the lineas naturales. Incipit not listed
in Thorndike and Kibre.]

xiv c., paper, 50 fols. Originally two separate mss.: (1) n.a. 2130,
comprising present fols. 1-22. Single cols. 13 x 7.8 cms., 31 lines,
written in single hand. Rubr. in red and blue. Contains (fols. 1-20^V)
Cicero, Epistole, and (fol. 21) a work beginning Quidem eloquens
Ganus de colle vulgarem sonettum misit .ff. petrarcho per linguam
cuiusdam. Fols. 21^V-22^V ruled but blank. (2) n.a. 773, comprising
present fols. 23-50. Single cols., written in two hands, of which the
first occurs in fols. 23-42, 15.5 x 8.5 cms., 28-29 lines; and the
second in fols. 43-50, 17.5 x 13 cms., 25 lines. Rubr. in orange
and red on fols. 23-42 only. Fol. 40 ruled but blank. In addition to
items a and b, listed above, this part of ms. contains (fols. 40^V-42)
specimens of Greek alphabet in the first of its two hands. Fol. 42^V
blank. Ownership notes: on fol. 42^V, Iste liber est gigo durandis
et . . . ; on same fol. in another hand, Iste liber est michi felice et
anthonio richardi que. On fol. 23 a more recent hand writes:
Aemilius Macer de Herbis—Item in fine voluminis habetur Tractatus de chyromantiae; and on same fol., Carthusiae Villae nouae
prope Auenionem.

63 (VIII. 63: Pieralisi I, 95; n.a. 1944).

Gaii publi solini viri doctissimi liber polinistor [sic] ubi
omnis antiquitatis mirancla [sic] sub compendio lecta
sunt. Incipit feliciter prologus.

Inc.: Quoniam quidam impaciencius pocius . . .   fol. 1
Expl.: nuncupationem sui congruere insularum qualitatem. Gaii Solini viri doctissimi polinistor Explicit feliciter. deo gratias.   fol. 99

[Ms. listed in ed. Mommsen (2nd ed., Berlin, 1895),
p. L, item 142, s.n. VIII. 63. Incipit not in Thorndike
and Kibre.]

xv c., parchment, 99 fols., single cols. 13.5 x 9 cms., 27 lines.
Written in single hand. Titles rubr. in red; ornamented initials in
blue, green, purple, yellow, grey, and gold; elaborate border on fol.
1, with arms of Francesco Piccolomini. Ownership note on fol. 1:

Francisci Marie Piccolominei episcopi Ilcinensis, cui Dominus
Adrianus Saracenus dono dedit, anno 1569, mense Augusto. Bound
in contemporary brown calf, blind stamped with Piccolomini arms.

68 (VIII. 68: Pieralisi I, 103; n.a. 2690).

A ms. of two texts, of which the first is relevant to the
present collection:

Pomponii Mele de cosmographia liber primus incipit.

Inc.: ORbis situm dicere aggredior impeditum . . .   fol. 1

Expl: promontorium operis huius. atque athlantici
littoris terminus./ Finis.   fol. 34^V

> [Prologue and bks. i-iii complete. See ed. Frick
> (Leipzig, 1880); and Schanz-Hosius, VIII. 2 (4th ed.,
> 1935), 656. Cf. below, MSS. 81 and 139.]

xv c., parchment, 57 fols., single cols. 14.5 x 8.5 cms., 26 lines.
Written in single hand. Fols. 35-37 contain Claudianus, De raptu
Proserpinae. Illuminated initials and on fol. 1 elaborate ornamented
border. On fol. 57 drawing of a galley by a later hand.

76 (VIII. 76; n.a. 800 et VII. C. 6.).

Described by Saxl, Verzeich. astrolog. u. mytholog. illustr. Hss.
(Sitzungsb. d. Heidelb. Akad., philos.-hist. Kl., vol. VI), pp. 4-5.
The ms., xv c., contains (a) Arati Genus (fols. 1-2^V), (b) excerpts
from Scholia sangerman. in Germ. Caes. Aratea (fols. 2^V-5^V),
(c) Germ. Caes. Aratea, vv. 1-514, cum Schol. sangerman. (fols.
6-66), (d) Arati Phaenom. reliq. (fols. 68-71), (e) excerpts from
Schol. sangerman. in Aratea de Sole et Luna (fols. 71^V-77),
(f) excerpts from Plini Nat. hist., bk. XVIII (fols. 77^V-85^V), (g) De
polis mundi (fols. 85^V-86), and (h) Plini Nat. hist., XVIII, 341-42,
and (i) Hygini Poet. astron., IV, 6-14 (fols. 86-100).

77 (VIII. 77; n.a. 2170).

Described by Saxl, Verzeich., pp. 6-7. The ms., xv c., contains
(a) Arati Genus (fols. 1-2), (b) excerpts from Schol. sangerman.
in Germ. Caes. Aratea (fols. 2-4), (c) Germ. Caes. Aratea,
vv. 1-430, cum Schol. sangerman. (fols. 4^V-41), (d) Arati Phaenom.
reliq. (fols. 41-43), (e) excerpts from Schol. sangerman. in Germ.
Caes. Aratea de Sole et Luna (fols. 43-46^V), (f) excerpts from

Plini Nat. hist., bk. XVIII (fols. 47-51^V), (g) De polis mundi (fols. 51^V-52), (h) Plini Nat. hist., XVIII, 341-42, and (i) Hygini Poet. astron., IV, 6-14 (fols. 52-59^V).

81 (VIII. 81: Pieralisi I, 118; n.a. 2577).

A miscellany containing one relevant item:

Pomponii Melle de Cosmografia liber incipit.

Inc.: ORbis situm dicere aggredior . . .   fol. 1

Expl.: promontorium operis huius. atque athlantici
littoris terminus. Liber Pomponii Mele de Cosmographia Tercius et Vltimus explicit.   fol. 24

[Prologue and bks. i-iii complete. This ms., once
the property of Holstenius, not in Almagià, L'opera
geografica di L. H. (Studi e testi no. 102 [Vatican,
1942]). Holstenius' will lists a Pomponius (see
Rabe, Zentralbl. f. Bibl., XII [1895], 443 ff., esp.
item 44) but as intended for the Vatican.]

xv c., parchment, 25 fols., single cols. 18 x 11 cms., 34 lines. Written in single hand. Contains, on fols. 24-25, Demosthenes oratorium
principis oratio ad Alexandrum . . . traducta de greco in latinum
per leonardum Aretinum; and, on fol. 25, the Epitaphium Homoniae
conjugis Atimeti. Rubr. in red. Signature on vellum fly leaf: Lucae
Holstenii.

92 (VIII. 92: Pieralisi I, 130; n.a. 830).

a) <Quotaecumque tabulae computi.>   fols. 1-2^V

Inc. text.: Si quis uero etiam calculandi . . .   fol. 1^V

[A series of computist tables, fols. 1^V-2^V, one of
which is entitled Tabula Bede.]

b) Incipit geometria EVclidis a Boetio in latinvm Hortatione
Symachi Geometrum Exercitissimi LVcidvs translata.

Inc.: Quia uero mi patrici geometrarum exercitissime
euclidis . . .   fol. 3

Expl.: quod sunt modia lx.   fol. 47^V

[Following text another hand writes Ponderis signa
uide, uersa pagella, and there are weight symbols
in marg. Present ms. listed in Thorndike and Kibre,
col. 574.]

<u>c</u>) [Bedae liber.] De loquela digitorum.

Inc.: Cum ergo dicis unum . . .   fol. 47^V

Expl.: faciunt solidos xv. hoc est libra.   fol. 48^V

> [Part of title in square brackets added by later hand.
> Present ms. listed in Thorndike and Kibre, col. 136,
> under De temporum ratione but as by Pseudo-Bede.
> See, however, C. W. Jones, Bedae pseudepigrapha
> (1939), pp. 22-23 and n. 2 and pp. 53-55; and Bedae
> opera de temporibus, ed. Jones (Med. Acad. Amer.,
> no. 41 [1943]), esp. pp. 329-31 and 333-35; both of
> which note the occurrence of chaps. 1 and 4 separately
> from Bede's treatise as a whole; chap. 1, as here,
> frequently in mss. from the viii c. onward.]

<u>d</u>) <Capitulum Isidori> De Ponderibus.

Inc.: Ponderis signa plerisque ignota sunt . . .   fol. 48^V

Expl.: litteram habens .O. coniuncta cenix est.   fol. 48^V

> [Etym., xvi. 22, "De signis." A later hand adds beside
> title, erroneously, Haec Beda, and at end Hoc opus-
> culum fragmentatum suis manibus scripsit. Incipit
> sometimes appears in non-Isidorean tracts (cf. Mesue
> ed. Lyons, 1533, fol. 345^V). Not in Thorndike and Kibre.]

xii c., parchment, 48 fols., single cols. 19.7 x 9.3 cms., 40 lines.
Written in single hand. Rubr. in red, with figures throughout item
<u>b</u>. Some gloses in marg. Old binding in brown calf, blind stamped
with flower designs.

103 (VIII. 103: Pieralisi I, 143; n.a. 831 and VII. D. 12).

<Fragmentum Euclidis Geometriae: Versio II, ut videtur,
Adelardi Batonensis cum additamentis et commento
Campani Novariensis.>

Inc. text.: Communicantes: est irrationalis: diciturque
superfities medialis; eiusque latus tetragonicum .s.
quod in eam potest: est irrationale. diciturque linea
medialis . . .   fol. 1

Inc. comm.: Sicut due linee ab et bc continentes super-
fitiem ac rationales potentia . . .   fol. 1

Expl. text.: <F>abricato quouis regularium corporum
sibi speram inscribere.   fol. 60

Expl. comm.: Ex tertio decimo itaque libro manifestum
est . . . speram quemadmodum propositum erat in-

scripsisse et cetera. [Explicit liber xv Elementorum
Euclidis.]   fol. 60

[Text and commentary begin, incomplete, in the midst
of bk. X, prop. 19, and end with bk. XV; see ed. Venice:
Erhardt Ratdolt, 1482, sigs. [i8] - [r7v]. See also M.
Curtze, in Euclidis Opera omnia, ed. Heiberg and
Menge, Supplementum (Leipzig, 1899), p. xiii, p. 302,
n. 1, et passim. The added words in square brackets
of the explicit are written in a more recent hand. For
the connection with Adelard of Bath see, e.g., H.
Weissenborn, in Abhandl. z. Gesch. d. Math., III.4
(1880); Crombie, Grosseteste and exper. sci. (Oxford,
1953), p. 52, n.6; and M. Clagett, in Isis, XLIV (1953),
20-23, and 29, n. 31 (4).]

xv c., parchment, 60 fols., single cols. 18.3 x 11.6 cms., 46 lines.
Written in single hand. Figures throughout in margins. On fol. 1
the same hand as that of the added words of the explicit writes:
Euclidis Geometriae liber 10 & 11 [sic]. cum comment. Campani;
and, est 19 propos. in edit. Basil pag. 262. (see ed. Basel:
Johannes Hervagius, 1537, pp. 262-478, the text ex traditione
Campani). Ownership note, fol. 1: Caroli Strozzę Thomę filii 1635.

130 (VIII. 130: Pieralisi I, 174; n.a. 1473 and XVI. B. 30.).

Martianus Foelix Capella Apher Liber primus. De nuptiis
cylleni et philologie.
Inc.: < >Ii [sic] quem psallentem . . .   fol. 1
Expl.: dactylicus per choricum qui ex similitudine
trochei uideatur . . .   fol. 112^V

[Ends incomplete at ix, 993; ed. Dick, p. 532,
ll. 1-2. Cf. above, MS. 10.]

xv c., paper, 112 fols., single cols. 20 x 12 cms., 35 lines, with
occasional double cols. for verse. Written in single hand. Mathematical figures in marg., fols. 76 and 76^V. Spaces for rubr. initials
but none executed. Fol. 1, bottom marg., has the monogram FS.

139 (IX. 8: Pieralisi I, 187-88; n.a. 812).

A miscellany containing one relevant item:
Pomponii Mela de situ orbis.
Inc.: VRbis [sic] situm dicere aggredior impedi-
tum . . .   fol. 1

Expl.: promontorium operis huius atque atlantici
   litoris terminus.   fol. 29

   [Prologue and bks. i-iii complete. Cf. above,
   MSS. 68 and 81.]

xv c., paper, 120 fols., single cols. 19.7 x 9 cms., 32 lines. Written
in single hand. Contains (fol. 1) Pomponius Mela, (fol. 31) Brevarium Sexti Rufi romanae historia, (fol. 40) Sexti Aurelii Victoris de
viris illustribus liber, (fol. 59) De Roma antiqua commentarium,
(fol. 88) In Persium commentarium anonymi, (fol. 103^V) De philosophia et philosophorum sectis, (fol. 107) De diphtongis et ortho-
graphia. Title of Pomponius written in later hand.

143 (IX. 12: Pieralisi I, 195; n.a. 2503).

   [LIBER. PRIMVS. PLINII SECVNDI. NATVRALIS HISTORIE.
   CAPITVLORVM. QVI ET PRIMI LOCO INTITVLATVR
   INCIPIT PROHEMIVM. SVPER TOCIVS OPERIS LIBRIS]
   Inc. elog. Suetoni: PLINIVS. SECVNDVS NOVICONIENSIS
      EQVESTRIBVS. MILITIE. INDVSTRIIS. FVNCTVS.
      PROCVRATIONES. QVOQVE. SPLENDIDISSIMAS.
      ATQVE CONTINVAS. SVMMA. INTEGRITATE.
      AMMINISTRAVIT . . .   fol. 1
   Inc. epist. dedic.: PLINIVS. Secundus. Vespasiano suo.
      Salutem. Libros naturalis historie nouitium camenis
      queritium tuorum . . .   fol. 1^V
   Inc. lib. I: [INCIPIVNT CAPITVLA LIBRI SECVNDI
      QVE SVNT CAPITVLA.]   fol. 3
   Inc. lib. II: MVNDVM. ET. HOC. QVOD. ALIO. NOMINE.
      CELVM. APPELLARE . . .   fol. 9
   Expl. lib. XI: quod graue quolibet modo utilius. Verum
      ad reliquam naturam transeamus. [EXPLICIT. DEO
      GRATIAS. AMEN. SVMMARES ET HISTORIE ET OB-
      SERVATIONES .824. PLINII SECVNDI NOVO COMEN-
      SIS. ORATORIS. EQVESTRI ORDINIS. NATVRALIS
      HISTORIE LIBRO .11. EXPLICIT FELICITER.]   fol. 152

   [Originally contained bks. I-XI entire but by loss of
   40 fols. (71-110) bk. VI now ends (fol. 70^V) incomplete
   in cap. 28 (ed. Jan-Mayhoff, VI. 26) with the words que

tamen babilonia cognominatur; bks. VII and VIII are
missing; and bk. IX begins (fol. 111) incomplete in
cap. XIII (ed. Jan-Mayhoff, IX. 15) with the words nec
nisi intrantes pontum biçançium. Incipits and explicits
in square brackets are by another hand. In the title
following HISTORIE the word VERONENSIS appears,
and following LIBRIS the words QVI CONTINET
LIBROS .XXXVII. ET FVIT EQVESTRI ORDINIS
MILES appear, but are deleted. In the elogium (fol. 1)
MILITIE and PROCVRATIONES are written with C,
corrected to T. For the elogium itself, often found
in mss. and early printed eds. of Pliny, see C.
Suetoni Tranquilli praeter Caes. lib. reliqu., ed.
Reifferscheid (Leipzig, 1860), pp. 92-93; cf. ed. Roth
(1871), pp. 300-301. The present ms. is evidently
unknown to modern editors and commentators. Some
cite Barb. lat. 2503 but that is MS. 177 below, which
happens to have the same n.a. See, e.g., ed. Sillig
(2nd ed., 1851), I, esp. xxi and lvii-ix, sub sig. z;
ed. Detlefsen (1866), esp. I, 3-11, and II, 3-6; ed.
Jan (2nd ed., 1870), I, viii-lxxxii, passim; ed. Mayhoff
(1892-1930), passim, but esp. III, viii; and ed. Beau-
jeu, Ernout and Pepin (Budé ed., 1947), I, 20-33 and
37-38, II, xx and 5, etc. Cf. Torre di Rezzonico,
Disquisitiones Plinianae (Parma, 1763-67). For the
commentators see Schanz-Hosius, Gesch. d. röm.
Litt. (4th ed., 1935), VIII. 2, 778; N.I. Herescu, Bibliog.
de la litt. lat. (Paris, 1943), pp. 329-30; and H. le
Bonniec, Bibliog. de l'hist. nat. de Pline (Collec.
d'études lat., ser. sc., n. XXI, Paris, 1946), pp. 13-15.
See also below, MSS. 162, 163, 177 and 180.]

xiii c. [?], parchment, 152 (originally 192) fols., single cols. 20.5 x
14 cms., 45 lines. Written in single hand but with incipits, explicits
and chapter headings in another and cruder script (see nn. on text
above). Rubr. in red and blue. At the beginning of each book elaborate initials with floral ornamentation indicate by their design the
Italian character of the ms. Some gloses in a xv c. hand in margins.

155 (IX. 24: Pieralisi I, 211; n.a. 792).

Incipit liber introductorius iudiciorum zaelis bembizir.

 israhelite. lege feliciter: —

Inc.: <S>cito quod signa sunt 12. et ex eis sex masculina

 et sex feminina . . .   fol. 1

Expl.: destruetur omne quod pertinet ad eandem domum

 et omnes res eius. Finis Explicit liber zahelis

 hisrahelite.   fol. 29^V

 [The words Finis . . . hisrahelite are rubr. and
 followed further by the title Incipiunt Capitula uel

<u>rubrice</u> and a list of chapters. As frequently in
mss. and printed eds., text brings together in one
body the three separate parts, which are usually
distinguished by the titles <u>Introductorium, 50</u>
<u>precepta,</u> and <u>De iudiciis;</u> see, e.g., ed. in <u>Quadri-</u>
<u>partitum Ptolomei</u> etc. (Venice: Hered. Oct. Scoti,
1509), fols. 111^V-25^V (present text lacks brief
final section, as found there, entitled <u>De signifi-</u>
<u>cationibus horarum planetarum in interrogationibus</u>).
Cf. V. Stegemann, <u>Dorotheos von Sidon und das so-</u>
<u>genannte Introductorium des Sahl ibn Bišr</u> (Mono-
graphien des Archiv Orientální, Bd. XI [Prague,
1942]), pp. 26-29, 35-58, <u>et passim.</u> See also
Steinschneider, <u>Sitzungsber.</u>, CLI (1906), 154, item
188a; Thorndike, II, 390-91 and nn.; Thorndike and
Kibre, col. 652; and Carmody, <u>Ar. astron.</u>, 3.1-3.
Cf. below, <u>MS. 256</u>, item <u>d</u>.]

xv c., paper, 29 fols., double cols. 22.1 x 6 cms., 51 lines. Written
in single hand. Section headings rubr. in red, and spaces left for
rubr. initials, which are, however, not executed. Some gloses in
margins. Another hand has written (fly leaf, recto) <u>Hilarens dato-</u>
<u>rem delegit Dominus,</u> and (fly leaf, verso) <u>Non aliam Domine</u>
<u>mercedem, nisi te ipsum.</u> On inside front cover the date <u>1667</u> writ-
ten in same hand as that of <u>n.a. 792.</u>

156 (IX. 25: Pieralisi I, 212-13; n.a. 2237).

<u>a</u>) Johannis de monte regio epithome in almagestum
Ptholomei.

Inc. dedic.: <A>DMIRANTI michi sepenumero uel
potius grauiter uel inique ferenti . . .   fol. 1

Inc. text.: Recte profecto meo iudicio nobiliores . . . fol. 2^V

[Expl. fol. 145. See Thorndike and Kibre, cols. 620
and 29.]

<u>b</u>) Incipit tractatus de compositione astrolabii secundum
dominum andalum de nigro Januesem et primo quid
sit astrolabium deinde imaginationes et considera-
tiones quas habuerunt compositores . . .

Inc.: Astrolabium est pars spere depresse forma ro-
tunda . . .   fol. 146

Expl. (mutil.): Sequitur de lineis quatuor principali-
oribus astrolabii.   fol. 147

[Ends incomplete; fols. 147^V-49^V ruled but blank.

Ms. listed in Boncompagni, Bullettino, VII, 359,
s.n. IX. 25.]

c) <Andali de Nigro Theorica distantiarum omnium
   sphaerarum.> <D>e centro et concentrico et ex-
   centrico et semidiametro et spera capitulum primum . . .

   Inc.: <P>Vntus centrum cuspis sunt sinonima . . .   fol. 150

   Expl.: latitudo umbre erit in illo loco minuta 46
   secunda 47.   fol. 155^V

   [Ms. listed in Boncompagni, Bullettino, VII, 363,
   s.n. IX. 25.]

d) <I>Ncipit theoricha planetarum composita ab andalo
   de nigro yanuense capitulum primum de figura mo -
   tus solis.

   Inc.: <Q>Via in teorica planetarum motus solis est neces-
   sarius . . .   fol. 162

   Expl.: in nodo capitis uel caude ubi maxima est declinatio
   diametri .h.k.   fol. 171^V

   [Ms. listed in Boncompagni, Bullettino, VII, 351,
   s.n. IX. 25.]

e) Liber auen alpetragi in astrologia <translatus per
   Magistrum Michaelem Scotum>.

   Inc.: <V>Olo dicere stellarum eraticarum et solis
   et lune. Et iam explanauit . . .   fol. 172

   Expl.: Perfectus est liber Auen alpetragi laudetur
   Yesus Christus. qui uiuit in eternum per tempora
   translatus a magistro michaele scoto tolleti. in
   decimo octauo die ueneris augusti hora tertia. cum
   abuteo leuite Anno Incarnationis Yesu Christi /m^o/
   cc^o/xxi^o Deo gratias Amen.   fol. 194

   [Cf. Al-Biṭrūjī, De mot. cel., ed. Carmody (Univ. of
   Cal. Press, 1952), esp. pp. 160 and 156-57. For significance of date see Haskins, Med. sci., pp. 273-74,
   and n. 9. Incipit not listed in Thorndike and Kibre;
   but see col. 330.]

f) <Messahallae Astrolabium translatum per Johannem
   Hispalensem.>

   Inc. prol.: <S>cito quod astrolabium sit nomen grecum

cuius interpretatio est acceptio stellarum . . . fol. 198

Inc. text.: <C>Vm uolueris facere astrolabium ad latitudinem cuiusque regionis . . . fol. 198

Expl.: cum uero loco qui fuit in radice et sic patet
propositum. fol. 215

> [Fol. 215^V ruled but blank. Cf. ed. Gunther, Early
> science, V, 195 ff. See also Björnbo, Bibl. math.,
> 3, XII, 195 and 199; Thorndike and Kibre, cols. 652
> and 164; and, for state of texts of this and other
> translators, Thabit b. Qurra, ed. Carmody (Berkeley,
> 1941), "Introd."; and Ar. astron., 26.1a. See below,
> MS. 276, items b and f and nn.]

xv c., paper, 215 fols. Composed of three parts: (1) Fols. 1-149 and
198-215, single cols. 23 x 12.5 cms., 32 lines, written in large
humanistic hand, on paper with cardinal's hat watermark. (2) Fols.
150-71, double cols. 23.6 x 6.6 cms., 54 lines, in smaller hand,
darker ink, on paper with cardinal's hat watermark but different
from (1). (3) Fols. 172-97, double cols. 22.6 x 6.55 cms., 48 lines,
in hand larger than that of (2), on paper having crowned male profile as watermark. Spellings in item e suggest Spanish origin of (3).
Rubr. in red uniform in all parts but incomplete: i.e. (1), fols. 198-
215^V, and (3), fols. 177-97^V, have none, but spaces are left for
initials. Ownership notes: On fol. 1, marg.: Bartholomej Vespuccij
quem emit anno 1512 florentie libre 3; and on fol. 217: Bartholomej
Vespuccij librum emi Florentie anno 1512 libre 3.

160 (IX. 29: Pieralisi I, 218-21; n.a. 767).

Described by Beccaria, I codici di medicina del periodo presalernitano (Rome, 1956), pp. 324-31, whose numbering is followed in
the present condensed account. His incipits are given with some
modification from the ms. For item 17 (Oribasius), which varies
in further detail, see ed. Mørland (Oslo, 1940). For the connection of items 6-10 with Cassiodorean tradition and its develop-
ment to the Carolingian period, see Courcelle, Les lettres
grecques en Occident (1943), pp. 382 ff.:

S.n.) Incipit liber medicine platonis ex herbis masculinis . . . quas
scolapius inuenit (Inc.: Plantago. Pentafilos; Inc. breues: Herba
uettonica), fols. 1-6^V.

1) Hippocrates, Epistula ad Maecenatem (Inc.: Ippocrates moece-
   nati suo), fols. 6^V-8.

2) Antonius Musa, De herba vettonica (Inc. epist.: Antonius musa.
   magno agrippe; Inc. text.: Nomen herbe uettonica), fols. 8-10.

3) Apuleius Platonicus, Herbarium (Inc. epist.: Apulius platon<icus>
   ad ciues suos; Inc. text.: Nomen herbe plantago), fols. 10-27^V.

4) Sextus Placitus, Liber medicinae ex animalibus (Inc.: Cornus
   cerui habet uires), fols. 27^V-38.

5) <Pseudo->Dioscorides, Liber medicinae ex herbis feminis (Inc.
   breues: 1. Herba hecinum.facit ad emoptoicos; Inc. text.: Nomen
   herbe hecinum), fols. 38-48^V.

6) Galen, De febribus, i.e. Ad Glauconem de methodo medendi lib.
   I-II (Inc.: Febrium species discernere), fols. 48^V-76^V.

7) Galen, Lib. III (Inc.: Cephalea est dolor capitis), fols. 76^V-88.

8) Aurelii Liber (Inc.: De quattuor humoribus qualiter egritudines
   faciunt. Omnibus hominibus generantur), fols. 88-94.

9) Aesculapii Liber (Inc.: Cephaloponia.uel capitis dolor), fols. 94-
   109.

10) Incipit liber galieni de podagra [= Alexander Trallianus, Thera-
    peutica, lib. XI] (Inc.: Podagricorum causas scire), fols. 109-12^V.

11) Antidotarium (Inc.: Antidotum adrianum maiorem), fols. 113-35^V.

12) De ponderibus <et> signis (Inc.: Talentus habet pondos), fols. 135^V-
    36.

13) <Pseudo-> Galen, Liber de urinis (Inc.: Inter cetera quae scripta
    sunt), fols. 136-38^V.

14) Alexander <Trallianus?>, De pulsibus et urinis (Inc. prol.: Aliqua
    superius scripta sunt; Inc. text.: Omnium causarum dum esset),
    fols. 138^V-41.

15) Dogma Hippocratis (Inc.: Corpus hominis diuisum est), fols. 141-
    42.

16) Commentum ad Libros aforismi Hippocratis, lib. I-VII (Inc. prol.:
    Medicina partitur; Inc. text.: Quia necesse est), fols. 143-98^V.

17) Incipit liber galieni [= Oribasius, Synopsis, lib. I, II, IV] (Inc. I:
    Ante exercitationem calefacere; Inc. II: Adianthus. Sparagus;
    Inc. IV: Aleum.Cepam), fols. 199-216.

18) Galen, Alphabetum ad Paternianum (Inc. pref.: Cum michi pro-
    posuissem; Inc. prol.: Hec sunt pater carissime paterniane; Inc.

text.: Aes hustum), fols. 216-35^V.

19) Theodorus Priscianus, Euporiston cum additamentis ex Pseudo-Theodoro et Pseudo-Plinio (Inc. pref.: Nuper me collige olimpi; Inc. prol.: Si medicina minus eruditi; Inc. text.: Spuma argenti sem. 1), fols. 236-65^V.

20) Quintus Serenus, Liber medicinalis (Inc.: Phebe salutiferum), fols. 266-74^V.

21) Hippocratis Epistula ad Antiochum regem [= Epistula Dioclis Carystii ad Antigonum] (Inc.: Hypocrates chous antiocho regi salutem. Quoniam conuenit te), fols. 274^V-75^V.

22) Vindicianus, Epistula ad Pentadium (Inc.: Vindicianus pentadio nepoti suo salutem. Licet sciam te), fols. 275^V-76. (Versio altera, fol. 288^{rv}.)

23) Incipiunt dies egyptiaci, fol. 276.

24) Antidotarium, fols. 276-81^V.

25) Sapientia artis medicinae (Inc.: Quattuor sunt uenti.quattuor sunt anguli celi), fol. 282^{rv}.

26) Isidore of Seville, Etymologiae, lib. IV (Inc.: Medicina est que corporis), fols. 282^V-86.

27) Dynamidia Galieni (Inc.: Vera hec est dinamis), fol. 286^{rv}.

28) Epistula (Inc.: Frustra mortalium genus), fol. 286^V.

29) <Pseudo->Hippocrates, Secreta (Inc. prol.: Peritissimum omnium rerum; Inc. text.: Si habuerit dolorem uel), fols. 286^V-87^V.

30) Iudicia valetudinum Hippocratis (Inc.: Si tinnitum aurium fuerit), fols. 287^V-88.

31) Quomodo visitare debeas infirmum (Inc.: Non omnem infirmum uniter), fol. 288.

32) Quomodo febrientem curare debeas (Inc.: Febres quam quidem multe sunt), fol. 288.

33) Vindicianus, Gynaecia (Inc.: Expositio membrorum quo ordine), fols. 288^V-89^V.

34) Formulae et fragmenta varia, fols. 142, 265^V, inter alia duo Inc. (fol. 276^{rv}): Boglossos herba agrestis, et Rafanum graeci nos radicem dicimus.

xi c. For details of the ms. see Beccaria, p. 324. On fol. 1 the note, cancelled out: Caroli Strozzę Thomę filii.

162 (IX. 31: Pieralisi I, 223; n.a. 759 and VII.B.2).

<Caii Plinii Secundi Naturalis Historiae Cum Indice
Locupletissimo Tomus Primus.>

Inc. epist. dedic. J. B. Palmarii: Nobilissimo Iuueni
Conssalo Ruitio De la uega & Mendoza . . . Palmarius.
Non quia magnum aliquid operosum . . .   fol. 2

Expl. epist. Palmarii: tibi praestare uelimus.   fol. 5^V

Inc. carmen ad lectorem: Qui Coelum: Terras:
Aequor: Genus omne animantum . . .   fol. 5^V

Expl. carmen: Auctori quantum saecula debuerunt.   fol. 5^V

Inc. text. Plini: Plinius secundus veronensis Vespasiano suo Salutem . . .   fol. 9

Expl. lib. XVIII: sudorem repositoriis linquentia diras
tempestates praenuntiant.   fol. 451

[Ends with Bk. XVIII, but see MS. 163 below. Fols.
6-9 contain various elogia in auctorem from Suetonius,
Tertullian, and Eusebius of Caesarea, together with
Pliny's epistle Tacito suo. The 10-line poem Ad lectorem (fol. 5^V) names Hermolaus Barbarus, the xv-c.
scholar-scientist, who used the present ms. in what
was the first critical discussion of the text: Casti-
gationes Plinianae (Rome, 1492); see ed. Sillig (2nd
ed., 1851), I, xxiii. The poem itself appears on the
title-page of C. Plynii Secvndi naturae historiarum
libri .xxxvii. E castigationibus Hermolai Barbari
(Venice: Georgius de Rusconibus, 1519), ed. by
Johannes Baptista Palmarius, the author of the dedication in the present ms. (fols. 2-5^V).]

xv c., parchment, 451 fols., single cols. 22 x 15 cms., 31 lines.
Written in single hand. Rubr. initials in red and blue. Title-page
and dedication to Cardinal Barberini (fols. 1-1^V), not originally
part of ms., were added in xvii c.: Caii Plinii Secundi Naturalis
Historiae Cum Indice Locupletissimo Tomus Primus; and, Francisco Barberino Cardinali Amplissimo Alexander Gallus. Iacobus
Gallus Parens meus (Eminentissime Princeps) post rectam spatio
. . . ex ciuitate Neapolis. Bound in red morocco with arms of
Cardinal Francesco Barberini in gold on both covers.

163 (IX. 32: Pieralisi I, 224; n.a. 760).

<Caii Plinii Secundi Naturalis Historiae Tomus Secundus.>
Inc. lib. XIX: Gaii Plinii Secundi Naturalis Historiae

Liber .XIX. . . . Prohemium. SYderum quoque tem-
pestatumque . . .   fol. 1

Expl. lib. XXXVII: quecunque ambitur mari FINIS.   fol. 384

[This is a continuation of text in MS. 162 above.
Fols. 384^V-388 ruled but blank. Present ms. unknown to Sillig (2nd ed., 1851), I, esp. xxiii, and
not mentioned by the other modern editors and
critics.]

xv c., parchment, [1]+387 fols., single cols. 22 x 15 cms., 31 lines.
Written in the same hand as MS. 162, of which it is a continuation,
and in all other ways like it. As in MS. 162 a title-page and dedication were added in the xvii c. (on a leaf s.n. in present numbering
and preceding fol. 1): Caii Plinii Secundi Naturalis Historiae Tomus
Secundus; and a six-line poem addressed to Francesco Barberini:
En ubi Romulei Alcides nouus Orbis Atlantis/ . . . Mox meritò dici
fortior Alter Atlas./ Alexander Gallus D.D. Title-page has a deco-
rated, flowered border with the Gallus arms. Bound like MS. 162
in red morocco with arms of Cardinal Francesco Barberini in gold
on both covers.

165 (IX. 34: Pieralisi I, 227-34; n.a. 731 and VII. A.1).

The corpus recentius of Aristotle and related texts: listed
      and analyzed in Lacombe, II, 1162-64, item 1717; q.v.
      To this analysis may be added the following details of
      items chiefly pseudo- and non-Aristotelian. They are
      here numbered in conformity with Lacombe:

3. Aristotilis philosophi de celo et mundo . . .   fols. 190-
                                                                 233^V

[At bottom of fol. 233^V is a diagram of the four
directions, winds, elements, seasons, humors,
ages: (1) septentrio, boreas, terra, autumpnus,
melancolia, senectus . . . etc.; and between each
wind are its two side winds, making 12 altogether.]

15. Incipit liber de causis cum commento secundum
      proclum:——

Inc. text.: Omnis causa primaria plus est influens . . . fol. 379

Inc. comm.: Cum ergo remouet secunda causa
      vniuersalis . . .   fol. 379

Expl. text.: est ens et generat<io> simul.   fol. 382

Expl. comm.: non acquisitum sicut ostendimus.

      Explicit liber de causis cum commento:-   fol. 382

38

[Translation of Gerard of Cremona. As in other mss.
text is conceived of as a series of key sentences, commentary as those passages which develop the sentences;
but present commentum has some Christianizing inter-
polation varying from ed. Bardenhewer (1882), pp. 54-
56, 140, 152-62, and nn. on pp. 163-91 passim; and
Lacombe, I, 94 and 196.]

22. <Liber Costa ben Lucae de differentia spiritus et animae.>

Inc. (mutil.): secunda anima igitur est perfectio

prima . . .   fol. 392

Expl.: et det tibi fortunam in hoc seculo et in futuro:-

Amen:- Explicit liber de differencia spiritus et

anime:-   fol. 392

[Evidently the Recensio anonyma, but with some
coincidences with John of Spain: see Lacombe, I,
94 and 197-98. For problem of translator, whether
John of Seville, see Thorndike, II, 74. Text begins,
incomplete, in chap. 3, ed. Barach (1878), p. 135,
l. 6.]

24. <Liber Secundi philosophi de Graeco in Latinum trans-

latus a Magistro Willelmo medico natione Provinciali.>

Inc.: SEcundus philosophus fuit hec philosophatus. In

omni tempore silencium seruans . . .   fol. 393

Expl.: bibliothece inseri et intitician [sic] secundi

phylosophi. Explicit secundus phylosophus:-   fol. 393^V

[See Thorndike, II, 487; and Hauréau, Schedario, s.v.
Secundus fuit, etc. See also Vincent of Beauvais, Spec.
hist., x. 70; and Demophili, Democratis, et Secundi . . .
sententiae morales, ed. Holstenius (1639).]

29. Incipit documentum aristotilis ad allexandrum discipulum

suum de modo custodiendi corpus suum diuersimode

secundum diuersitatem temporum:——

Inc.: OPortet te alexander cum a sompno surrexeris

moditer ambulare et equaliter . . .   fol. 402

Expl.: Qui similis lac et pisces comedit lepeam aut

maculas albas incurrit. vinum et lac simul ad

inuicem comparantur:- Explicit epistola aristotilis

ad allexandrum regem suum discipulum. anno domini

.1288. finitus fuit. anno domini .1000. et .200. et 88.

fuit completus iste liber.   fol. 402^V

[Text of John of Spain corresponding to <u>Secreta secre-</u>
<u>torum</u>, II. iv-xiv, ed. Steele, <u>Opera Rogeri Baconi</u>, V
(1920), 68-83; and varying from ed. Suchier, <u>Denk-</u>
<u>mäler prov. Lit. u. Spr.</u>, I (1883), 475-80, and Lacombe,
I, 93-94 and 196. For title see R. Foerster, in <u>Cen-</u>
<u>tralbl. f. Bibliotheksw.</u>, VI (1889), 71-75. For problem
of identity of translator see Thorndike, II, 76. None
of these lists present ms.]

30. Incipit tractatus de fluxu maris Boecii.

   Inc.: INtendentes de accessione et recessione maris et

   primo de causa materiali que duplex est . . .   fol. 402^V

   Expl.: naturaliter generat colorem ut patet ultima pro-

   positione de speculis—Explicit tractatus de fluxu

   maris:-   fol. 403

   [The work of Robert Grosseteste: see Pelster, in
   <u>Scholastik</u>, I, 576 f.; and S. H. Thomson, <u>Grosse-</u>
   <u>teste</u> (1940), p. 89. Present text incomplete, containing first half of book only. Not in Thorndike
   and Kibre.]

31. Incipit tractatus de yride Boecii.

   Inc.: Et perspectiui et phisici est speculatio de

   yride . . .   fol. 403

   Expl.: credibilia uideantur experimento cum et racione

   clarescunt:- Explicit tractatus de yride:-   fol. 404

   [The work of Robert Grosseteste: see ed. Baur,
   Beiträge, IX, 72-78; and Thomson, p. 106.]

34. Incipit tractatus de fractionibus wlgaribus:-

   Inc.: MVltiplex est modus scribendi huius artis .scilicet.

   in numeracione minuciarum uulgarium . . .   fol. 405^V

   Expl.: et sic .2. integrorum aut radix cubita igitur et

   sic de aliis:- Explicit tractatus algoristicus de

   fractionibus wlgaribus:-   fol. 406^V

   [Incipit not in Thorndike and Kibre.]

35. Incipit tractatus de figuris geomancie:-

   Inc.: Sciencia diuiditur in theoricam et practicam/

   theorica in rationalem et realem. realis in mathe-

   maticam/ mechanicam/ et phisicam . . .   fol. 406^V

   Expl.: secundum nomen et proprietatem similiter et

   cardines confortantes.:- Explicit tractatus de

figuris geomancie. fol. 407

[Incipit not in Thorndike and Kibre.]

36. Incipit tractatus <pseudo-Aristotilis> de figuris tem-
   pestatum:- <Versio non, ut videtur, Bartholomaei de
   Messana sed cuiusdam innominati.>
   Inc.: SIgna aquarum et tempestatum . . . fol. 407
   Expl.: aues que uiuunt in insula aquam signant.:.-
   Explicit liber de signis tempestatum:- fol. 407^V

   [A fragment of the variant translation coinciding
   with Oxford, Corp. Chr. MS. 243, fols. 52-53. Cf.
   below, MS. 303, item 1. Incipit in Thorndike and
   Kibre for the Bartholomaeus text only.]

Late xiii or early xiv c., parchment, 415 fols. For general description of ms. see Lacombe. The fragmentary items 14 (Physica),
21 (De proprietatibus), and 22 (De differentia), at one time evidently complete, have suffered from subsequent losses of leaves, e.g.
an entire gathering between items 21 and 22 (fols. 391^V-92). At end
of item 14 is the catchword hominis and the number xxxiiii' (fol.
378^V); and numbers xxxvi' and xxxviii' occur on fols. 394^{V}and 414^V.

166 (IX. 35: Pieralisi I, 235-36; n.a. 1697).

a) In nomine patris et filii et spiritus sancti. liber incipit de
   consolatione medicinarum simplicium solutarum quem
   fecit Johannes heben mesuhe.
   Inc. prol.: In nomine dei misericordis cuius nutu sermo
   recipit gratiam. fol. 1
   Inc. text. cap. i: Dicimus quod medicina laxatiua non
   est . . . fol. 1
   Expl.: Dosis eius est a karatis .vj. usque ad .3. .ij. uel
   ad tres. deo gratias. fol. 24^V

   [Cf., e.g., Mesue, ed. Lyons, 1533, fols. ii ff.]

b) Incipit antidotarium Johannis mesuhe. comm<entatum
   [?] >.
   Inc.: SCRIPSIMus in libris explanatiorum nostra-
   rum . . . fol. 25
   Expl.: Et quanto est antiquius. tanto melius./ Finem

41

huius grabadim accipit locus iste. Quare gratias
omnium largitore bonorum referimus qui auxili-
atur nostris laboribus et statuit lumen in tenebris
et labore quietem. fol. 42

[Cf., e.g., ed. Lyons, 1533, fols. xlii-lxxxiv^V.]

<u>c</u>) Incipiunt secreta experimenta Galieni.

<u>Inc.</u>: ROGASTI me amice montee . . . fol. 42^V

<u>Expl.</u>: galieni et gloriosioris benedictionis quam libri
eius alii . . . Explicit liber secretorum experimentorum .G. ad monteum amicum Deo gratias. fol. 47^V

[Text preceded on fol. 42 by rubric <u>Incipiunt Capitula</u>
<u>libri experimentorum Galieni</u> and a list of chapter
headings. Cf. ed. Junta, VIII (<u>Spurii Galeno ascripti</u>
<u>libri</u>), 101^V- 8^V, and Thorndike, in <u>Journal of the</u>
<u>History of Med. and Allied Sc.</u>, VIII (1953), 275. See
Thorndike, II, 758-61 and 775-76; and Diels, I, 146,
and III, 41; neither of which lists present ms.]

<u>d</u>) Incipit tractatus de aptatione medicinarum ut sine orri-
bilitate possint summi secundum rasym ℞.

<u>Inc.</u>: PIllule mirobalanorum que sunt composite non
uolentibus . . . fol. 48

Incipit alter tractatus de ornatu facierum mulierum
secundum rasim. capitulum primum de medicinis
que ornant faciem.

<u>Inc.</u>: MEDICAmen ad remouendum maculas nigras . . .fol. 48

<u>Expl.</u>: cum mucillagine psillii deo gratias. Expliciunt
tractatus de aptatione medicinarum et de ornatu
mulierum et ornatu capillorum secundum rasim.
deo gratias. fol. 48^V

[This work sometimes appears in mss. and early eds.
either as part of the <u>Experimenta Rasis</u> or as opening
chaps. of the <u>Antidotarium Rasis</u>: see Thorndike, II,
753-54 and 771-74; and, e.g., ed. Venice, 1508, fols.
95^{V}ff., and ed. Basel, 1544, pp. 540-51, which attributes the Latin version to Gerard of Cremona. Title
and incipits not in Thorndike and Kibre.]

<u>e</u>) In nomine dei misericordis Johannis nazarez filii mesuhe
grabadin medicinarum particularum incipit/ quid est
grabadin sufficiente medici et perfectionum. Inquid

johannes mesuhe.

Inc.: SAnat solus languores deus. et de . . .   fol. 49

Expl.: Et cura est similitudinaria cure pluresis deo

gratias Amen.   fol. 84^V

[Text corresponds to that of ed. Lyons, 1533, fols.
86 ff.]

f) Fragmentum medicinale.

Inc. (mutil.): non pascat . . . Si absens sit tumor . . .   fol. 85

Expl. (mutil.): scripsit quodque sepissime rescriptum

est. quamdiu unus ex$\overline{co}$ fol. 85

xiv c., parchment, [1] + 85 fols., double cols. 24.3 x 6.9 cms., 53
lines. Written in single hand. Rubr. in red and blue, with illuminated
initials at beginning of each tract in violet, red, green, blue. Fol.
85^V blank, but on unnumbered leaf bound in at beginning of ms. are
lists of simples and recipes in several later hands.

171 (IX. 40: Pieralisi I, 241-42; n.a. 766).

a) Sinonima magistri simonis de ianua super uniuersos libros
in medicina de greco et arabico in latinum. <Cum episto-
lis Simonis et Campani.>

Inc. epist. pr.: Domino suo precipuo magistro campano
domini pape capellano canonico parisiensi. symon
infimis subdiaconus se ipsum ex debito. Opusculum
a nobis iamdudum postulatum . . .   fol. 1

Inc. epist. alt.: Venerabili uiro magistro symoni
ianuensi domini pape subdiacono et cappellano canonico Rotomagensi amico suo carissimo tamquam fratri.
Campanus eiusdem domini pape cappellanus canonicus
parisiensis salutem. et quidquid est optabile sane
menti.   fol. 1

Inc. prol.: Optabat .V [?]. discere et docere posse res
sine nominibus . . .   fol. 1

Expl. prol.: Grecum uero alfa. in nullo a nostro .a.
differt potestate.   fol. 2

Inc. text.: Abantib. et alcutub. uel. cutub. seu cutubub.
arabice . . .   fol. 2

Expl.: Zurimbet . . . odore et sapore zedoarie remissis
tn. Benedictus deus in donis suis. et sanctus in omnibus operibus suis. Explicit sinonima Magistri Simonis
de janua. fol. 114^V

[Cf. below, MS. 333, item a. Title and incipits, except
for epistola prima, not in Thorndike and Kibre (see
col. 475).]

b) <Carmen astrologicum de medicina.>

Inc.: Nil capiti facies aries dum luna refulget . . . fol. 115

Expl.: Embrio conceptus exilenticus exit ab aluo. fol. 115

[Fols. 115-16^V were originally blank; present poem
of 36 verses added in later hand. Cf. Thorndike and
Kibre, col. 430.]

c) Liber <Platearii> que dicitur circa instans de simplicibus
medicinis.

Inc. prol.: Circa instans negotium in simplicibus medicinis . . . fol. 117

Inc. text.: Aloen. calide. est. et sicce complexion-
is . . . fol. 117

Expl.: Ne uero presentis operis prolixitas diffundatur
hoc in loco finem concludimus. Explicit liber de simplicibus medicinis que dicitur circa instans. fol. 157^V

[Cf., e.g., ed. Venice, 1497, fols. 186 ff.]

d) Incipit liber de simplicibus medicinis compilatus a con-
stantino phylosophie discipulo et montis cassini mona-
cho atque subdito.

Inc. prol.: QVia disputationem custodiende [sic] sanitatis . . . fol. 158

Inc. text.: Oportet autem medicum egritudines
curare . . . fol. 158

Expl.: Zedoara. calida est . . . allea accipiatur et in
ore maxticatus [?]. fol. 192

[The present work differs from the book entitled De
simplicium medicinarum virtutibus, as it appears in
Opera Isaaci (ed. 1515) and in the mss. described by
Henschel in Janus, I, 76, and Steinschneider in Virchows Archiv, XXXVII, 396-401. For incipit of pro-

logue cf. **De Inamidiarum (Dynamidarium) Galieni** in Cambridge, Gonville and Caius MS. 411 (415), fols. 169-201^V.]

e) Incipit liber alchindi de simplicibus medicinis: tractatus primus de medicinis in primo gradu qualitatum.

Inc. prol.: QVoniam simplicis medicine disputationem . . .   fol. 193

Inc. text.: Rosa frigida est in primo gradu sica . . .   fol. 193^V

Expl.: Titimalli. calidi sunt et sicci in .1111°. gradu . . . mastice et cum melle potentur. Explicit liber Alchindii Deo gratias. [de simplicibus medicinis] Explicit liber alchindi de simplicibus medicinis.   fol. 209^V

[Constantinus Afer, De gradibus quos vocant simplicium liber. A list of chaps. precedes prologue. Bracketed words of the explicit added in a later hand. Cf. Constantini . . . opera, ed. Basel, 1536, pp. 342-87. See Steinschneider, in Virchows Archiv, XXXVII, 361-63; and Thorndike and Kibre, cols. 591-92 and 632, under Constantinus and Isaac Judaeus (?).]

f) Incipit liber macronis de simplicibus medicinis et primo de artemisia.

Inc.: Erbarum quasdam dicturus carmine uires . . .   fol. 209^V

Expl.: Posse. licet uires uideratur habere minores.

Explicit liber macronis Deo gratias.   fol. 222

[Cf. above, MS. 56, item a. Fol. 222^V blank.]

xiv c., parchment, 222 fols., double cols. 24.8 x 7.4 cms., 50 lines. Written in single hand (but see above, item b). Rubricated in red and blue throughout. To this ms. have been bound the following items: Fol. 223, Troparii fragmentum saec. xv ("Gloria in excelsis" cum tropis); fol. 225, Gloria in excelsis deo, tribus vocibus, saec. xv; and, fol. 226, Henrici <Rampini> tituli S. Clementis presbyter card. et Mediolanensis archiepiscopi atque in tota prouincia Lombardiae . . . fragmentum epistolae missae Bernardo de Carreto abbati Sancti Quintini de Spigno.

72 (IX. 41: Pieralisi I, 243-44; n.a. 791 and VII. C. 3.)

a) Incipit haly habenragel de Judiciis astrorum in omnibus
quatuor partibus. Liber primus de Interrogationibus.

Inc. prol.: In nomine dei. Hic est liber magnus et com-
pletus/ quem aly abenragel filius summus astrologus
composuit de iudiciis astrologie/quem ihuda filius
musce precepto admodum illustris regis castelle transtulit de arabico in maternum. uidelicet yspanicum
ydioma. et quem petrus de regio magne et imperialis
aule prothonotarius una cum egidio. de thebaldis par-
mensi ipsius aule notario transtulit in latinum . . . fol. 1

Inc. text.: Dixit ali filius abenragel gratias vni deo
uictorioso honorato . . .   fol. 1

Expl.: Et quid futurum est melius nouit deus. Hic
explicit liber completus in iudiciis stellarum
quem composuit Albohazen aly filius abenragel de
quo laudem/ et gratias ago per simpiterna secula
deo patri/ amen. Finito libro isto referamus⸐ gratia
Christo.   fol. 187^V

[A list of 60 chaps. follows the prologue. Cf. Thorndike and Kibre, col. 212 et al., which does not, however, record present ms. or the translator from
Arabic into Spanish, ihuda filius musce. See also
Carmody, Ar. astron., 28. 1a.]

b) <Fragmentum nativitatis quam ponit Ali ibn Ridhwan in
fine Quadripartiti.>

Inc.: VOlo dicere exempla ut melius intelligas . . .   fol. 187^V

Expl. (mutil.): dedi ei uim meridianam/ et quia erat
in opposito.   fol. 187^V

[No title, but another hand notes in marg. Ista est
illa natiuitas quam ponit haly abenrodan in fine
quadripartiti. Cf., e.g., ed. Venice, 1519, fol. 95,
col. 1. Fragment ends, incomplete, in midst of
opening sentence of chap. "De statu patris." Fol.
188 blank.]

c) <Praedictio horribilis ad annum 1329 per Magistrum
Johannem Davidem Tolletanum.>

Inc.: Omnibus ad quos presens . . .   fol. 188^V

Expl.: Hec autem audiuimus a Rege Ciruli/ que uobis

periculosa uidentur. Valete. Tradita erat hec. Cantori . . .
Parisiensi. anno domini .1322. in die beati Jacobi apo-
stoli et transmissa domino Henrico de Vrtalis Canonico
traiectensi——   fol. 190

[Cf. V. Rose, Hss.-Verzeichn. Berlin, Lat. Hss., II.
3 (1905), 1079-80; Thorndike, II, 75-76, n. 3, and III,
322, n. 92; and Brit. Mus., MS. ad. 16606, fol. 112.]

d) Tabula circularis de introitu solis in arietem et ceteris
   signis . . .   fol. 190^V

   Expl. text.: ad cuius tabule expositionem subsequitur
   breuis Canon tam de formatione ipsius tabule . . .
   Quia igitur constat ex premissis quod annus solaris
   est redditus solis et cetera.   fol. 190^V

   [A table with explanatory text.]

xiv c., parchment, 190 fols. Written in at least four hands: (1) Fols.
1-42, double cols. 28.2 x 8.4 cms., 60 lines; (2) fols. 42^V-138,
double cols. 27.9 x 8 cms., 56 and 53 lines (the shift in lines occurs
within a gathering); (3) fols. 138-90, double cols. 26 x 7.3 cms.,
varying 53 and 50 lines within gatherings; (4) fol. 190^V. Rubr. in
red, blue, and purple. Some gloses in several later hands. On fol. 1,
col. 1, another hand adds a table with the description: Et est figura
mitii huius translationis/ die Jouis .12. mensis martii .21. die
mocharam era Arabum .692. Christi .1293. Cesaris .1291. Allexan-
dri .1999. On inside of back cover: In nocte sequenti diem Mercurii
que fuit vigesima nona Martii Anni 1447. Erant quidem luna et
Jupiter circa lineam Meridiei. luna tamen erat septentrionalior.
Et erat Altitudo Cent' lune .55. gradus. Et Jouis .54. gradus./ et
.30. minute. Et Cordis leonis .56. gradus. In vrbe Rome. (There
follows a list of Italian cities—from Florence to Cumae—with the
signs under which they fall.) Various ownership notes only partly
legible, including: Eugenii Ioannis . . . filius ex Mei . .onis libris
. . . hunc librum Bybliothece . . . pr clarique . . . patri memoriam
dicende . . . erauit.

73 (IX. 42: Pieralisi I, 245; n.a. 790 and VII. C. 2.).

Incipit almagesti quem ptolomeus pheludensis de scientia stellarum et motuum celestium conscripsit. <Liber translatus

per Gerardum Cremonensem cum additamentis e versione
altera de Arabico.>

Inc. lib. I, 1 e vers. alt.: BOnum quidem fecerunt⸍ in eo quod
uideo illi qui perscrutati sunt . . .   fol. 4

Expl. lib. I, 1 e vers. alt.: neque consequuti sunt ex eius
comprehensione quod oportet.   fol. 4^V

Inc. prol. pr. Gerardi: QVidam princeps nomine albu-
guafe . . .   fol. 5

Inc. prol. alt. Gerardi: LIber hic precepto maimonis
regis arabum . . .   fol. 5

Inc. lib. I, 1 Gerardi: BOnum domine fuit. quod sapientibus . . .   fol. 5^V

Inc. lib. IV Gerardi: Iam narrauimus et demonstraui-
mus . . .   fol. 49

Inc. nota de lib. IV e vers. alt.: Nos quia peruenimus
in tractatu qui est ante hunc . . .   fol. 49,
                                                       marg.

Expl. lib. XIII Gerardi: tunc iam sequitur et honestum est ut ponamus hoc finem libri. Explicit.   fol. 185

[Gerard's version with long extracts, usually marked
in alio or aliter, in marg. throughout from a second
translation from the Arabic: cf. Florence, B. n., MS.
conv. soppr. J. IV. 20; and see Haskins, Med. sci.,
pp. 105 - 8, which does not, however, list present or
Florentine ms. MS. Vat. lat. 2057, noted in Nogara's
catalogue and Haskins as having alternate chap. 1,
also contains similar extensive extracts in marg.,
passim. Cf. below, MS. 336. Unbracketed part of title,
as given above, appears on fol. 5; and on fol. 4 a
modern hand writes Almagestum Ptolomei Pheludensis. Table of contents, fols. 1-2^V; fol. 3 blank.]

xiv c., parchment, 185 fols., double cols. 25.4 x 6.2 (varying to 26.2
x 6.2) cms., 45 and 46 lines. Written in single hand, with marg.
notes in second but similar hand. Tables and figures throughout.
Rubr. red and red and blue. Binding stamped in gold with arms of
Card. Francisco Barberini, and Barberini bees on spine.

177 (IX. 46: Pieralisi I, 249; n.a. 2503).

<C. Plini Secundi Naturalis historiae libri XXXVII.>

Inc. elogium Suetoni: Equestribus militię industriis functus.
procurationes quoque splendidissimas . . .   fol. 1

Inc. epist. dedic.: Historię nouitium Camenis quiritium
tuorum opus natum apud me . . .   fol. 1

Inc. lib. I: Caii secundi Plinii historiarum mundi ele-
mentos. Librorum omnium xxxvii: Liber unus qui
Primus: Libro secundo continetur . . .   fol. 2^V

Expl. lib. XXXVII: proxime quidem dixerim hyspaniam
quocunque ambitur mari. Plinii secundi Nouocomen-
sis naturalis historię libri .xxxvii. finiuntur. Scripti
Romę a me Bernardo petri de Basilea clerico con-
stantiensi diocesi. Terminati quoque die quinta mensis Maii. Anno dominicę incarnationis .M^o. CCCC^o.
LXVIII°. LAVS. DEO.   fol. 391

[Collated in ed. Sillig (2nd ed., 1851), sub sig. z (see
I, xxi and lvii-ix); and ed. Jan (2nd ed., 1870), pp. viii
ff.; and also, for the elogium alone (fol. 1), in Suetonius, Praeter Caesarum libros reliquiae, ed. Reifferscheid, pp. 92-93 and notes. It should be noted that the
n.a. 2503 is the same as that for MS. 143 above (q.v.),
which suggests that the two texts were once associated
in the Barberini library, though they are of entirely
separate origin. See also MSS. 162, 163 above, and
180 below.]

xv c., paper, 393 fols., single cols. 26.6 x 18.1 cms., 47 lines.
Written in the year 1468 by Bernardus Petrus de Basilea (as above).
Fols. 392-93 ruled but blank. Rubr. in red and blue, with initials
ornamented in flower patterns in red, blue, white, yellow, green,
and gold. Fol. 22, containing the beginning of bk. II, has an elaborate multi-colored ornamental border with foliage, birds, croco-
diles, genii, etc.

78 (IX. 47: Pieralisi I, 250-52; n.a. 1690).

a) <Galeni Liber therapeuticae sive methodi medendi translatus per Burgundionem Pisanum cum additionibus
Magistri Petri de Abano.>

Inc.: Tarapenticam [sic] methodum eugeniane amicissime
olim quid inceperam scribere . . .   fol. 3

Expl.: Expletus est liber tarapentice cum additionibus
Magistri Petri de Ebano. que deficiunt ex translatione
burgundionis ciuis pisani. Deo gratias. Anno domini
.M.CCC.xxviiii. die .vi^a. maii.   fol. 44^V

[= Θεραπευτικῆς μεθόδου βιβλία ιδ΄. No title, but running heads <u>GA</u> (= Galen), <u>PE</u> (= Petrus), and the numerals <u>VII</u> through <u>XIIII</u>. See Haskins, p. 208, n. 103; and Thorndike, <u>Isis</u> XIII, 87, item 75, and XXXIII, 652, n. 23. Ms. <u>not in</u> Sante Ferrari, p. 150, nor in Diels, I, 92-93.]

<u>b</u>) <Galeni Liber de complexionibus translatus per Gerardum Cremonensem.>

Inc.: SVmme que sunt in sermone libri primi . . .   fol. 45

Expl.: Explicit liber de complectionibus .tres. Anno domini .M^o .ccc^o.xxviiii^o. die .v^a. agusti.   fol. 58

  [= Περὶ κράσεων. No title, but running head <u>De Compl'</u> and the numbers of the books. Following the explicit another hand adds: <u>Qui scripsit scribat semper cum domino uiuat.</u> See below, <u>MS. 179</u>, note to item <u>c</u>. Ms. not listed in Diels, I, 65.]

<u>c</u>) Incipit liber G<aleni> de accidenti et morbo <translatus per Constantinum Africanum [?]>. Capitulum. primum. prohemiale. in quo manifestat quod intendit . . .

Inc.: In inicio huius libri diffinire morbum oportet . . .fol. 58

Expl.: Explicit liber Galieni De Accidenti et morbo. Deo gracias. Amen. Anno domini .m^o.ccc^o.xxviiii^o. die .xxi. Sectembris.   fol. 73

[For the Galenic originals of this work see Diels, I, 136-37, and III, 40, which do not, however, list the present ms. The text varies from that of <u>MS. 179</u>, item <u>e</u>, below. For the ascription to Constantinus see V. Rose, <u>Die Hss.-Verzeichn. d. Königl. Bibl. z. Berlin</u>, II. 3 (1905), 1058 and indexes to <u>MS. Elect. 897</u>, fols. 128-54.]

<u>d</u>) Incipit liber G<aleni> de crisi. Capitulum prohemiale in quo suam intentionem declarat.

Inc.: EGo non intendo in hoc meo libro . . .   fol. 73^V

Expl.: Expletus est tractatus de crisi. Deo gracias. Amen. Anno domini .m^o.ccc^o.xxx^o. die .xiiii^a. mensis marcii. tempore sancte quadragessime.   fol. 91^V

[= Περὶ κρίσεων βιβλία γ΄. Ms. not in Diels, I, 90.]

<u>e</u>) <Carmen de temperamentis, etc.>

Inc.: De natura pingues isti sunt atque iocantes./ Senper

rumores cupiunt. senperque frequentes./ Hoc uenus
et bachus delectant. secula risus [?] . . .   fol. 92

Expl.:   consolidant alte .t'. bal. caumaia.
    Consolidancia   mirta.

                          lingnarum c̃anes. gipsus. balaus-
                          tiam. galla.   fol. 92^V

[Based in part on the <u>Regimen sanitatis Salerni</u>, but
otherwise a different work; see <u>Regimen</u> (Frankfurt,
1559), cap. 88, fols. 229^V ff.; ed. I. Reichborn-Kjenne-
rud (Halden, 1932), cap. 86, pp. 42 ff.; and ed. Barbensi
(1947), p. 21 f. Cf. below, <u>MSS. 186</u>, item <u>d</u>; <u>311</u>, item
<u>b</u>; and <u>3957</u>. Not listed in Thorndike and Kibre.]

<u>f)</u> <Galeni Liber de differentiis febrium translatus per
    Burgundionem Pisanum.>

<u>Inc.</u>: Differentie febrium que quidem proprie maxime
    principalissime sunt . . .   fol. 93

<u>Expl.</u>: uel digerantur/ uel utrumque paciantur. Explicit
    liber de differentiis. Febrium.   fol. 101^V

[= Περὶ διαφορᾶς πυρετῶν βιβλία β΄. See Thorndike and
Kibre, col. 200; Haskins, p. 208, n. 98; and Diels, I,
80. But none of these lists the present ms.]

<u>g)</u> <Averrois Liber de venenis.>

<u>Inc.</u>: Omnes species mortiferorum parciuntur in duo
    genera . . .   fol. 102

<u>Expl.</u>: cum condito ꝗuchaĩ. et ellixirium ipsorum. et illo
    utatur:/ Expletus est iste liber qui fuit auerroys.   fol. 102^V

[Cf., e.g., ed. Bologna, 1497-1500 (?).]

<u>h)</u> Incipit liber .G<aleni>. de malicia complexionibus diuerse
    <translatus per Gerardum Cremonensem>. Capitulum
    .primum. in quo ponit diuisionem et subdiuisionem
    malicie complexionis diuerse . . .

<u>Inc.</u>: MAlitia complexionis diuerse quandoque in toto
    corpore . . .   fol. 103

<u>Expl.</u>: intelligat librum meum de medicinis. deinde post
    ipsum librum de ingenio sanitatis. Explicit liber .G.
    de malitia complexionis. Deo gracias.   fol. 104^V

[= Περὶ ἀνωμάλου δυσκρασίας. Cf. Thorndike, in <u>Byzantina</u>

i) Incipit tractatus de diebus criticis secundum astrologos/
   editus perusii anno Christi 1358 per uenerabilem virum
   Dominum Fratrem Vgonem de Ciuitate Castelli/ ordinis
   predicatorum et Episcopum mire in astrologia peritum.

Inc.: Sicut dicit commentator super . . .   fol. 105

Expl.: Et uocatur similitudo quando plura mascu-

linum . . .   fol. 106

[On fol. 105 a large circular figure of the dies critici.
See Thorndike, III, 217, n. 17; Isis XIII, 76, item 46,
and n. 24; and The Sphere of Sacrobosco, p. 36, n. 57.]

xiv c., parchment, 107 fols. Fols. 3-107, double cols. 27.2 x 7.4
cms., 53 lines. Written in single hand. Dates in the explicit of items
c and d very much smaller but apparently in same hand. Rubr. in
red and blue. Item i written in different hand over another text by
original scribe which has been deleted. The deleted work, dealing
with matters of time-reckoning, cannot be completely read; where
it can it begins: siue una compacta. Et quoniam annus communis
habet lunationes .xii. Et quoniam annus . . . est habet lunationes
xi9. et incipuit a mense sectembri. quia in hec mense incipit . . .
lus dece nouenalis. i . . . Text appears to end on fol. 107^V: aGusti
acť.xxv. die. in die. in hor' .vi. et p̄ d .ccclxxxv. Annis adde monas
dm̄ partire per ūde Viginti. lune ciclus eiūde patet. Original ms.
began at fol. 3, to which were added present fols. 1 and 2, palimp-
sests containing fragment of a decretum, over which (fol. 2^V) a
later mediaeval hand has written table of contents that includes
present item i. On fol. 2^V note of ownership: Et est mey Marini
Jacobi de fermo . . .

179 (IX. 48: Pieralisi I, 253-56; n.a. 1691).

a) Incipit liber .G<aleni>. de complectionibus <translatus per
   Burgundionem Pisanum>. cuius sunt tres tractatus. primus est de esse complectionis et de differentiis seu
   generibus eius. et habet 4^{or}. doctrinas. prima est de
   esse complectionis. cuius .i^m. capitulum in quo . . .

Inc.: QVoniam quidem ex calido et frigido. et sicco et
   humido. animalium commista sunt . . .   fol. 1

Expl.: quemadmodum et in farmaciis ipsis/ dicendum est
ante. Explicit liber Galieni de complectionibus. Translatus a Burgundione Ciue pisano. secundum Nouam
Translationem. Deo gracias. Amen.   fol. 14^V

[= Περὶ κράσεων, See Haskins, p. 208, n. 95. Incipit
listed in Thorndike and Kibre, col. 603, but without
attribution to Burgundio. Ms. not in Diels, I, 64.]

b) INcipit liber .G<aleni>. de notitia locorum patientium/
qui nuncupatur liber de interioribus que loca sensu
occultantur/ per sex. genera figurarum . . . <Trans-
latus per Burgundionem Pisanum.>

Inc.: LOCa autem nominant particulas corporis non
iuniores solum . . .   fol. 15

Expl.: sed iam finem habente preiacente opera/ Hic
faciam quiescere sermonem. Explicit liber Galieni
de Interioribus/ secundum Nouam Translationem
Burgundii. Deo gratias. Amen. Amen.   fol. 36^V

[= Περὶ τῶν πεπονθότων τόπων βιβλία ζ′. See Haskins, p. 208,
n. 99. Incipit listed in Thorndike and Kibre, col. 392,
but without attribution to Burgundio. Ms. not in Diels, I,
86.]

c) Incipit liber .G<aleni>. de uirtutibus naturalibus. liber
primus. Capitulum primum in quo .G. distinguit animam
et naturam:—

Inc.: QVONIAM Sentire quidem et moueri secundum ele-
mentationem . . .   fol. 37

Expl.: uel nequaquam uniuersaliter uel omnifariam
euellunt breue. Explicit liber Galieni de Virtutibus
naturalibus. secundum Nouam Translationem. Deo
gracias Amen: —— Qui scripsit scripbat semper cum
domino uiuat. Amen.   fol. 56^V

[= Περὶ φυσικῶν δυνάμεων. For the motto Qui scripsit
etc. see note to MS. 178, item b, above. Ms. not in
Diels, I, 66.]

d) <Galeni Libellus de marasmo translatus per Nicolaum
Rheginum.>

Inc.: MArasmus est corruptio uiuentis corporis in

53

siccitate. fol. 57

Expl.: iam secundum artem habent/ scriptus est. Explicit
libellus Galieni de Marasmo secundum Translationem.
Deo gracias Amen. fol. 60^V

[= Περὶ μαρασμοῦ. Cf. Thorndike, in Byzantina metabyzantina, I.1, 226, no. 27. Ms. not in Diels, I, 83, and
III, 32.]

e) Incipit liber .G<aleni>. de egritudine et synthomate qui
diuiditur. in sex libros. quorum duo primi sunt de
egritudine reliqui de synthomate . . .

Inc.: PRimo quidem dicere oportet quid utique egritudinem
uocamus ut sit manifestum pro quo studet scrip-
cio . . . fol. 61

Expl. (mutil.): Vniuerse igitur magne discrasie pro-
sternunt uirtutem/ sed que in fr'o . . . fol. 86^V

[Incomplete, ending near the first part of lib. vi,
cap. 3. For the Galenic originals of this work see
Diels, I, 136-37, and III, 40, which do not, however,
list present ms. Version differs from that of MS.
178, item c, above. Cf. Erfurt, MS. Amplon. F 278,
fol. 55: Primo quidem dicere oportet . . . (see W.
Schum, Beschreib. d. Amplon. Hss.-Samml. z.
Erfurt [Berlin, 1877], p. 187).]

f) <Galeni Liber de accidenti et morbo.>

Inc. summa prima (mutil.): dominante [?] frigiditas
paxionum nate sunt operari. Que uero in calido
contrarias . . . fol. 87

Inc. summa secunda: Ad detentam autem uirtutem . . . fol. 87

Expl.: Hic igitur et hunc terminemus sermonem.
Explicit liber .G. de accidenti et morbo. secundum
Nouam. Translationem. fol. 92^V

[Opening lost; begins near end of Summa prima.
For Galenic sources see item e and MS. 178, item
c, above. Ms. not listed in Diels, I, 136-37.]

g) Incipit liber .G<aleni>. de Iuuamento Hanelitus. Cuius
sunt due summe. Summa prima in qua determinat de
opinione que est anelitus . . .

Inc.: CALorem uitalem quem in corde dicit Aristotiles
nutriri a sanguine pingui et uentuoso . . . fol. 93

54

Expl.: Solum enim aristotiles. in libro quod de parti-
culis animalium deligentur super hoc scripsit. Ex-
plicit liber .G. de Iuuamento Anelitus.   fol. 96^V

[Cf. Galen, ed. Junta (1609), VIII, fols. 63-65^V. Ms.
not listed in Diels, I, 137.]

h) Incipit libellus de lege Ypocratis.

Inc.: MEdicina artium preclarissima. Propter disciplinam
intentium . . .   fol. 96^V

Expl.: nequaquam prius quam secretis scientie perfici-
antur. Explicit libellus de lege ypocratis. Deo gratias.
Amen—   fol. 96^V

[See Thorndike and Kibre, col. 403.]

i) Incipit libellus afforismorum/ Johannis Damasceni.

Inc.: LIBERET te deus fili amantissime a deuio
erroris . . .   fol. 97

Expl.: Ego quod te huius primum unum et ualde gaudeo
cerno [?] translationem. Expliciunt afforismi Johannis
Damasceni.   fol. 99^V

[Cf., e.g., Articella, ed. Lyons, 1525, et al.]

j) Incipit liber Auicenne. de Viribus cordis. et de medicinis cordialibus. Translatus a magistro Arnaldo
barchione <sive de Villanova> . . .

Inc.: CReauit deus ex concauitatibus cordis sinistram
aurem ut esset . . .   fol. 99^V

Expl.: finem huic operi imponentes cum laude dei qui
uirtutem largiri dignatus est opusculum terminandi.
Explicit libellus siue opusculum Auicenne de viribus
cordis. et de medicinis cordialibus. Deo gracias
Amen.   fol. 108

[See B. H<aureau>, "Arnauld de Villeneuve," Hist.
litt. d. l. France, XXVIII, 98; E. Lalande, Arnaud
de Villeneuve: sa vie et ses oeuvres (Thesis: Paris,
1896), esp. pp. 191, 192, 194, 195; and Arnau de
Vilanova: Obres catalanes, ed. Battlori (Barcelona,
1947), II, 19. None of these lists present ms.]

k) <Pseudo-Hippocratis Capsula eburnea.>

55

Inc.: PEruenit ad nos quod cum Ypocrates morti appro-
pinquaret precepit . . .   fol. 108

Expl.: que inuenta est in sepulchro eius in piscide eburnea.
Et sunt .21. propositiones. Explicit opusculum de secretis .ypocratis. Deo gratias Amen Amen: — finito
libro sit laus et gloria Christi. Amen.   fol. 108^V

[Cf., e.g., ed. Venice, 1508, I, 41^V ff.]

l) Incipit liber .G<aleni>. de spermate . . . <Translatus per
Nicolaum Rheginum.>

Inc.: QVe est utilitas. et uirtus spermatis . . .   fol. 109

Expl.: quidem non tamen ueraciter Sicut nos super mon-
strauimus. Explicit liber de spermate. qui etiam dicitur de zoogonia .i. de generatione animalium.
Translatus de greco in latinum a Nicolao de Regio de
Calabria. Deo gratias Amen.   fol. 116^V

[= Περὶ σπέρματος βιβλ. β´. Translation not always ascribed to Nicholas of Reggio elsewhere: cf. Diels, I,
70; and Thorndike and Kibre, col. 551; see also
Thorndike, Byzantina metabyzantina, I.1, 230, no. 43.]

m) Incipit opusculum .G<aleni>. de causis respirationis.
<Translatum per Nicolaum Rheginum.>

Inc.: Respirationis causas sermo preiacens . . .   fol. 116^V
Expl.: quemadmodum uictorie retinaculi tetricis.

Deo gratias Amen.   fol. 116^V

[= Περὶ τῶν τῆς ἀναπνοῆς αἰτίων. Ms. not in Diels, I, 70.
Cf. Thorndike, Byzantina metabyzantina, I.1, 221-
22, no. 8.]

xiv c., parchment, 116 fols., double cols. varying from 28 x 8 cms.,
41 to 61 lines. Written in several similar hands, among which
quires were divided for copying. Fols. 109-16 on somewhat
smaller leaves but apparently part of original volume, since rubr.
throughout, in red, blue, and purple, are in same style. Modern
vellum binding with Barberini bee stamped in gold on spine.

180 (IX. 49: Pieralisi I, 257; n.a. 758 and VII. B. 1).

PLINII. VERONENSIS. SCRIPTORIS. ELEGANTISSIMI. NA-
TVRALIS HISTORIE. LIBRI PRIMI PROHEMIVM. INCIPIT.

FELICITER.

Inc. epist. dedic.: Libros naturalis hystorie. nouitium

camenis quiritium tuorum . . .   fol. 1

Expl. lib. XIII: si refellerint insidiae in lapidem trans-

figurari: —   fol. 188^V

[Collated in ed. Sillig (2nd ed., 1851), sub sig. y
(see pp. xxi and lvii-ix); and ed. Jan (2nd ed., 1870),
pp. viii ff. Cf. MSS. 143, 162, 163 and 177 above.]

xv c., parchment, 188 fols., single cols. 27.5 x 16 cms., 41 lines.
Written in single hand. Rubr. in red with initials illuminated in
elaborate branch and flower patterns in pink, green, white, blue
and gold. Title page (fol. 1) has intricate border of birds, animals,
insects, putti, etc., in red, blue, green, grey, white, purple and
gold; together with a male profile in a triangle and the arms of
the Gallus family within a double circle on the lower border (see
MSS. 162 and 163 above). The initial L of Libros of epist. dedic. is
illuminated with a fine portrait representing Pliny holding a green
book, and is signed: 1464. Benedictus. F<ecit>. Bound in contemporary brown leather over wooden boards and blind stamped with
ornamental borders.

182 (IX. 51: Pieralisi I, 259-60; n.a. 789).

a) Prologus primus in Almagesto ptholomei pheludensis
        <e translatione Gerardi Cremonensis> —

Inc. prol. pr.: Quidam princeps nomine albugnafe . . . fol. 3

Inc. prol. alt.: Liber hic precepto maimonis regis

arabum . . .   fol. 3

Inc. cap. 1: Bonum fuit scire . . .   fol. 3

Expl.: ut ponamus hoc finem libri. Expleta est dictio
XIII^{ma}. libri ptholomei. et cum ea completur liber
Almagesti de disciplinalibus. Omnipotenti gratiarum
acciones referendo.   fol. 99

[See, e.g., Haskins, Med. sci., pp. 105-6. Cf. above,
MS. 173, and below, MS. 336. Fols. 99^V-102^V originally blank, but see below, item f.]

b) Theorica magistri campani Novariensis.

Inc.: Primus phylosophie magister ipsius negotium in

tria . . .   fol. 103

<u>Expl.</u>: luna non retrogradatur Et istius capituli subditur
figura etc.   fol. 124

[See <u>Abhandl. z. Gesch. d. Math.</u> (1912), p. 128. Fol.
124^V originally blank, but see below, item <u>g</u>.]

<u>c</u>) Incipit liber haly alhamet de electionibus horarum
      <translatus per Platonem Tiburtinum et Savasordam>.
<u>Inc.</u>: Rogasti me karissime vt tibi librum . . .   fol. 125
<u>Expl.</u>: Perfectus est liber in electionibus horarum lauda-
      bilium editione Haly filii Achami Embrani translatus
      de Arabico in latinum in Civitate Barchinonia ab Abra-
      ham Iudeo Hispano qui dicitur Salva corda. existente
      interprete et perfecta eius translatio die lune 8. kal.
      Octobris vigesima quarta die mensis lunaris qui dictus
      est dulchida hora duodecima ascendente Aquario anno
      domine millesimo centesimo tricesimoquarto.   fol. 132

[For date and significance for Plato of Tivoli see
Haskins, <u>Med. sci.</u>, p. 11, and n. 30. Cf. ed. Millás
Vallicrosa, <u>Las traducciones orientales</u> . . . (Madrid,
1942), pp. 328 ff.; Björnbo, <u>Bibl. math.</u>, 3, XII, 103;
Suter, <u>Abhandl. z. Gesch. d. math. Wiss.</u>, X, 56-57;
and Carmody, <u>Ar. astron.</u>, 24.1a. Cf. below, <u>MS. 256</u>,
item <u>b</u>, <u>328</u>, item <u>q</u>, and <u>335</u>, item <u>a</u>.]

<u>d</u>) <Liber Haly de significationibus planetarum in domibus.>
<u>Inc.</u>: Incipiunt significationes planetarum . . .   fol. 132
<u>Expl.</u>: et proferes aliud et inuenies si deus voluerit.   fol. 133

<u>e</u>) <Quotaecumque sententiae, quaestiones, et figurae
    astrologicae, e.g.>
<u>Inc. sent.</u>: Romanorum Sententie 1. Non expedit tibi nec
      ducem vxorem. 2. Contrahe amicitiam. quia fidelem
      inuenies . . .   fol. 1
<u>Inc. quaest.</u>: 1. An sit bonum ducem vxorem/ An sit
      vtile contrahere amicitiam . . .   fol. 1^V
<u>Inc. veritates</u>: Veritas eterna est deus . . . Felicitas
      consistit in se ipso . . .   fol. 2^V

[The <u>sententiae</u> are arranged, ten each, for some twenty-
three "nations." Following the last, Granate, is <u>Finit.
Liber. Stella</u>; after which are other aphorisms headed
<u>Ad soldanum babilonis</u>. The <u>quaestiones</u> are accompa-
nied by "data" arranged in 4 cols. under the letters <u>Na</u>,

Ne, Ni, No; Ba, Be, Bi, Bo; etc. And on fol. 2 are 20
circular figures arranged in accordance with these
data. Following the veritates on fol. 2^V is a series of
horoscopes, arranged under each planet, from Saturnus to Luna. For the place of item e and the following
items in the ms. see general description below.]

f) <Excerpta astrologica varia ex scriptoribus Arabicis:>

[1] Tebith. Electiones. De Ymaginibus.

Inc.: Cum a ceteris cursus . . .   fol. 99^V

[2] De Interrogationibus . . .

Inc.: Sunt. mansiones. fortes . . .   fol. 99^V

[3] Libro mulierum. Capitulo 3°.

Inc.: Quid cr'[?] fetum faciunt stelle errantes.   fol. 100

[4] Speculum.

Inc.: Albertus dicitur magnus. Due sunt sentencie

astronomorum . . .   fol. 100^V

[5] Ysagoge tebit. in astrologiam.

Inc.: Equator diei est circulus maior . . .   fol. 101

[6] Philosophia/ Ad philosophiam naturalem et
mathematicam.

Inc.: Signorum. zodiacus. enim. circumferentia . . . fol. 102

[The last excerpt continues on fol. 102^V, then on
lower marg. of fols. 103-10^V. For Ysagoge tebit
see Thorndike and Kibre, col. 236; and Carmody,
Ar. astron., 18.2a.]

g) <Quaestiones astrologicae, e.g.>

De Negotiis agendis. Vtrum sint vtilia. Signa prime
domus . . . Vtrum duo amici se diligant . . .   fol. 124^V

h) In reuolutionibus annorum Albumasar uel floribus
eorum que significant res superiores in rebus . . .

Inc.: Dixit primum oportet te scire . . .   fol. 136

[Cf. below, MS. 303, item f.]

xv c., paper and parchment, 138 fols. Original ms., comprising
present paper fols. 3-136 (older numbering designates these 1-134),
written in two similar hands: (1) Fols. 3-99, double cols. 28.7 x 8.5
cms., 70 lines. (2) Fols. 103-33, double cols. 28.5 x 8.7 cms., 80
lines. Thus original contents were items a-d. Subsequently 2 parchment fols. each were added at beginning and end, and the whole re-

numbered as at present. On new fols. and on original blank leaves
and marg. another hand wrote items _e-h_; and in addition a piece
on the natures of the planets, aspects, etc. on fol. 132^V and marg.
of fols. 133-36. On fol. 137^V an elaborate figure with 12 branches
for 12 tribes, virgins, martyrs, confessors, intellectual virtues,
etc.; and with angels, zodiac signs and planets; all in an elaborate
cosmological pattern. On fol. 133^V, marg., and on inside back cover
medical recipes. Original rubr. red and blue through fol. 119^V,
thenceforward red only. Astronomical tables and figures throughout (fols. 119-24, circular spaces for figures, which are lacking).
On fols. 3, 103, 125, 132, and inside front cover, titles and table of
contents (items _a-d_) variously in two modern hands. On fol. 1, top,
the date 1452; fol. 2^V, col. 2, Magrī filippi cēnij d' Florētis; fol. 3,
marg., Caroli Strozzę Thomę filij 1635.

186 (X. 4: Pieralisi I, 264-66; n.a. 807 and VII. C. 19).

A miscellany containing the following Latin scientific texts:

_a_) <Kalendarium lunare ad annos 1493 et seq., i.e. duo figurae
circulares cum explicatis.>

Inc. text. pr.: Ad inueniendam literam dominicalem et
literam bisextilem per annos domini . . .   fol. 1

Inc. text. alt.: Ad inueniendum aureum numerum .id est.
cursum lune secundum ecclesiam et per annos
domini . . .   fol. 1

[Incipits not in Thorndike and Kibre.]

_b_) <Tabula cum explicatu mortis Latislai principis.>

Inc. text.: Quem rerum munda . . . postea latislaus incli-
tus filius romanorum alberti regis neposque Cesaris
Sigismundo in festo sancti clementis letifero de cibo
expirauit in praga etate bis nouem annorum . . .   fol. 1^V

Expl.: speratum in celis coniugii cristus uetatus
amen.   fol. 4

[Throughout the table is in the left-, the text in the
right-hand, column. Not in Thorndike and Kibre.]

_c_) <Opus astrologicum de medicina.>

Inc.: Notandum coniunctionem lune vsque ad oppositionem

lune Farmacie et Euacuacione 8 sunt faciem . . .   fol. 7

[Not in Thorndike and Kibre. Expl. fol. 39^{V}.]

d) <Libellulus medicinalis de quattuor temperamentis
   et eorum qualitatibus.>

   Inc.: Sanguineus ueluti Richardus de florentino [sic] dicit
   in sequente Largus amans rubeus colore . . .   fol. 40

   Expl. (mutil.): dent commedere cibaria.   fol. 41^{V}

   [Cf. above, MS. 178, item e; and below, MSS. 311,
   item b, and 3957. Not in Thorndike and Kibre. Fol.
   42 blank.]

e) Sequitur de annis quomodo se habebunt.

   Inc.: Quando festum natiuitatis . . .   fol. 43

   Expl.: frumentum satis erit —   fol. 43

   [Not in Thorndike and Kibre.]

f) Notabilis practica in studio parisiensi per astrologos
   secundum cursum planetarum et elementorum ex
   quibus videri potest et cognosci natura hominis ex
   aspectu.

   Inc.: Cum videris hominem in te visum frequen-
   tare . . .   fol. 43^{V}

   Expl.: declinantes ad rubidinem aspectum mites/
   Τελος   fol. 45^{V}

   [Not in Thorndike and Kibre.]

g) <Arnaldi de Nova Villa [?] > De Virtute quercus.

   Inc.: <R>Euerendo in Christo patri ac domino. Richardo
   diuina prouidencia episcopo Cantuariensis Magister
   arnoldus de noua Villa medicine artis et literarum
   experiencia professor . . .   fol. 45^{V}

   Inc. cap. pr.: Arbor quereus dulcissima fuit ab
   antiquis . . .   fol. 46

   Expl.: et vna die insolubiliter curatur etc. Τελος   fol. 48^{V}

   [See Lalande, Arnaud de Villeneuve, pp. 195-96;
   Hist. litt. d. l. Fr., XXVIII, 114-15; and Arnau,
   ed. Battlori, II, 45; the last two of which doubt
   the attribution to Arnaldus. None of these works
   lists present ms.]

h) \<Kalendarium sanitatis.\>

Inc.: In iano claris calidesque . . .   fol. 48^V

Expl.: sit tepidus potus frigoris contrario totus.

Τελος.   fol. 49^V

[A series of verses, four for each month.]

i) \<Johannis de Merliano Tractatus de pestilentia.\>

Inc.: Vt noscas te infectum pestilentia . . .   fol. 49^V

[Present ms. cited in Thorndike and Kibre, col. 744.
Expl. fol. 52.]

j) Dies lune.

Inc.: Prima die videlicet lune creatus est Adam . . .   fol. 52^V

Expl.: Trigesima natus fuit samuel . . . si nascitur

astutus erit——Finiunt die lune:.-   fol. 54^V

[See Somnia Danielis in Gesamtkat. d. Wiegendr.,
esp. nos. 7919-35.]

k) \<Capitulum astrologicum de xxxiv pericula.\>

Inc.: Notandum quod in anno sunt xxxiiii pericula sic

a magistris parisius et ab astrologis peruisum . . . fol. 55

Expl.: December habet tres scilicet 6/7/21/   fol. 56

[Not in Thorndike and Kibre.]

xv c., paper, 78 fols. Written in various hands, with scraps of
parchment and paper of various sources and sizes bound in. In
addition to the items above the ms. contains (1) fols. 5^V-6, recipes
in a dialect of the lower Rhine beginning Om perkement te maken
alsse claer als glas; (2) fols. 56-64, a group of 24 letters in Latin
without names of authors or addressees, chiefly from Milan but
also from Florence, Cremona, and Siena, dated by month but not
year (fol. 64^V blank); (3) fols. 65-75, another text in a dialect of the
lower Rhine beginning Sot ionck sot. Ou ionck/ Ou sot; and (4) fols.
75-75^V a group of accounts. Names of modern owners on fols. 75^V,
76, and 77^V.

196 (X. 14: Pieralisi I, 275; n.a. 2694).

a) \<Tabula remediorum.\>

Inc.: A. Medicina restaurans Auditum admissum c̃a

1 . . .   fol.[1]

Expl.: Electuarium ad raucedinem Vocis c̃a 31. Ad

idem. fol.[29ᵛ]

[An alphabetical list from A to V of chapter headings
for a book of cures. Fols. [30]-[33] blank. On fols.
[33v]-[45ᵛ] are the tables of an astrological calendar.]

b) <Tractatus astrologicus secundum signa et tempora.>

Inc.: Aries primum signum et est cauendum capud et

facies . . . fol.[46]

Expl.: Qui iiiᵃ die mensis minuerit infra xl' dies moritur

sine dubio. Tonitrus habundantiam singificat [sic]. fol.[57]

[Text is headed by a table of the signs entitled Aureus
numerus, and on fol. [57ᵛ] is a table of planets. Not in
Thorndike and Kibre.]

c) <Carmen astrologicum.>

Inc.: Audax vrbanus malus anticus fur . . . fol.[58]

Expl.: In uultu rubeum justum castum factiosum. Notandum

quod quiscumque natus . . . Proprietas planetarum

talis est Volentem ducunt nolentem trahunt resisten-

tem dimittunt [sic = dimicant?] :— fol.[58]

[13 verses with a brief prose comment at the end.
Not in Thorndike and Kibre.]

d) <Duo figurae circulares cum explicatu.>

Inc. text. pr.: Si uis reperire literam dominicalem . . .fol.[58ᵛ]

Inc. text. alt.: Si Vis reperire cursum aurei nu-

meri . . . fol.[59]

[Not in Thorndike and Kibre.]

e) <Kalendarium lunare cum explicatu.>

Inc. text.: Ratio lune sunt: 19. littere alfabeti incipiendo

ab. a . . . fol.[66]

Expl. text. (mutil.): in margine ante mensem Januarii

. . . ā. quanque fol.[66ᵛ]

[The calendar begins on fol. [60]. Not in Thorndike
and Kibre.]

f) <Collectus compendiosus remediorum.>

Inc.: <A>d restituendum obliuioni incomodo quod primus

senectutis impetus in nobis imprimit . . . Emplastrum

63

mirabile in vulneribus capitis et fractione cranei.
℞. bettenice . . .   fol. 1

[Collection begins with the rubr. Animata. Expl.
fol. 198. Not in Thorndike and Kibre.]

xv c., parchment and paper, [66] + 198 fols. Written in various
hands and of various sources. Ms. originally contained only fols.
1-198, 1-194 in parchment, 195-98 in paper (Pieralisi I, 275, lists
only these fols.). To them have been added the 66 unnumbered
leaves of mixed paper and parchment containing items a-e. On
fol. 131^V the hand of item f has written a group of medical verses
in Italian beginning Chi uol star sano obserui questa norma and
signed .P. de .E.

216 (X. 34: Pieralisi I, 295-97; n.a. 774).

a) <Collectus formularum medicinarum.>
   Inc.: Epithia per soda callida facta euacuatione cum
      rebus digerentibus . . .   fol. 1

   [Expl. fol. 2^V. Not in Thorndike and Kibre.]

b) <Alberti de Zacariis de Bononia Liber de cautelis
   medicorum habendis.>
   Inc. prol.: Quoniam nobis fortunam multas approbationis
      occasiones immittit . . .   fol. 3
   Inc. cap. 1: Medicus uulgaribus non multum . . .   fol. 3
   Expl.: multum omni fauore [sic] insurges etc. Explicit
      liber de cautelis medicorum habendis editus per ma-
      gistrum albertum de zacariis de bononia etc.—   fol. 5

   [Present ms. not in ed. M. Morris, Albertus de
   Zancariis (Leipzig: med. diss., 1914), nor its refs.;
   for which see esp. pp. 7-9.]

c) Albuberti arasi filii zarcharie liber incipit qui ab eo
   uocatur almansorius eo quod regis mansoris Ysaac
   filii precepto editus sit. <Liber translatus per Gerardum
   Cremonensem.>
   Inc. prol.: Verba albuberti. In hoc libro aggregabo
      regi cuius uitam . . .   fol. 6
   Inc. text.: CReator omnium deus ossa condidit. ut per

ea corpus . . .   fol. 9

Expl.: R/. piretri et sinapis. castorei . . . commiscean-
tur et fiet unguem.   fol. 119^V

[Cf., e.g., ed. Venice, 1508, I, 2 ff.; and Carmody,
Ar. astron., 22.2. Prologue varies from ed. Basel,
1544, and Thorndike and Kibre, col. 321, as ascribed
to Gerard. For Gerard as translator of Rasis see
Steinschneider (1905), p. 25; and Boncompagni,
Gherardo Cremonese, p. 6. Table of contents on
fols. 6-9.]

d) Incipiunt diuisiones rasis filii zacarie. <Liber translatus per Gerardum Cremonensem.>

Inc.: VEntilata fuit in presentia cuiusdam . . .   fol. 120

Expl.: aceti et olii añ quod sufficit.   fol. 173^V

[Cf., e.g., ed. Venice, 1508, I, 59^V ff. Text varies
from ed. Basel, 1544, as ascribed to Gerard. See
item c above.]

e) Incipiunt expositiones libri almansoris et libri
diuisionum.

Inc.: Baurach. i.e. omne genus salis . . .   fol. 174

Expl.: ponatur modicum de simplissima benedicta [?].
Explicit.   fol. 179^V

[Not in Thorndike and Kibre.]

f) Tractatus primus breuiarii filii serapionis medici translatus a magistro gerardo cremonensi. de arabico in
latinum.

Inc.: Inquid iohannes. INcipiamus cum auxilio dei. et
bonitate . . .   fol. 180

Inc. cap. 1: Egritudines iste . . .   fol. 180

Expl.: Completum est postremum aggregati ex libro
medicine iohannis filii serapionis.   fol. 363^V

[Cf., e.g., ed. Venice, 1479. See Steinschneider (1905),
p. 26; and Boncompagni, Gherardo Cremonese, p. 6.]

g) Incipit sisalaracer liber .s. quem composuit magister
zacharias de passionibus oculorum.

Inc.: Liber iste deinceps uocabitur panthachinatis .i.
speculationum . . .   fol. 363^V

Expl.: et tunc curabis si signa septa apparuerint.

Explicit. fol. 364^V

[Zacharias of Salerno, bk. III. Text varies from
that of ed. Pansier (Coll. ophthal. vet. auct., fasc. V
[1907]), pp. 88 ff., which does not list present ms.]

h) <Capitulum> De minutione.

Inc.: Minutionum alia per methathesim. alia per antipasim.

per methathesim dicitur fieri quando ex eadem parte

. . . Per antipasim quando ex porte contraria . . . fol. 364^V

[Expl. 367^V. Not in Thorndike and Kibre.]

i) Expositio membrorum principalium in uso materno. et

quo ordine. et quibus numeris. et quibus iuncturis.

uel quo scemate plasmetur.

Inc.: Maioribus nostris. luppo. ypocrati. apollonio . . . fol. 367^V

Expl.: quantoque fuerint deteriores tanto algescere

firmitatem. fol. 369^V

[Based on Vindicianus, Gynaecia. Cf. item m below,
and above MS. 160. See Sudhoffs Archiv, VIII, 417-23;
and Priscianus, Euporiston, ed. Rose, pp. 426 ff.;
neither of which lists present ms.]

j) Demonstratio medicamentorum in vniuersali.

Inc.: Bera [sic] demonstratio medicamentorum omnium

que ad artem medicine . . . fol. 369^V

Expl.: ex his duobus libris pigmentorum omnia melius

integra facies. Explicit. fol. 370

[Not in Thorndike and Kibre.]

k) Liber iacob alchindi philosophi de gradibus.

Inc.: Incipit uerbi ipsius. Quia primos ueteres ut de

uirtutibus . . . fol. 370

Expl.: dedi maiora parte miscitur [?]. Explicit. fol. 378^V

[Cf., e.g., Mesue, ed. Lyons (1533), fols. 345^V ff.;
and Carmody, Ar. astron., 12.17.]

l) De obseruatione lunationum quantum ad incisiones.

Incipit obseruatio lune quantum ad minutiones secun-

dum diuersa membra.

Inc.: Si luna fuerit in ariete . . . fol. 378^V

Expl.: et .iii kal'. feb'. et iii id' feb'.   fol. 379

[Not in Thorndike and Kibre.]

m) Amonitio magistri medici ad suum discipulum quod debeat
   facere.
   Inc.: Interea moneo te medice sicut . . .   fol. 379
   Expl.: salus a deo ueniet qui est medicus solus.   fol. 379

   [The prologue to De corpore humano et eius morbis,
   sometimes ascribed to Isidore and based on Vindicianus, Gynaecia: see item i and above, MS. 160. But
   cf. MS. Bruxell. 3701-3715 (x c.), fol. 7: listed in
   Diels, I, 53, among the Epistulae variae of Hippocrates.]

n) Epistola ypocratis ad mecenatem.
   Inc.: Quoniam cognouimus te . . .   fol. 379
   Expl.: aptum inuenerit corpus curet. Explicit.   fol. 380

   [Cf. Brit. Mus. MS. Add. 8928 (xi c.), fol. 11^V; listed
   in Diels, as above, item m.]

o) Quibus de causis prohibendus est uomitus.
   Inc.: Multi [sic] de causa prohibendus est uomitus:
   primo si . . .   fol. 380
   Expl.: radicem enule teneas in ore.   fol. 380^V

   [Not in Thorndike and Kibre.]

p) Incipit liber constantini de coitu.
   Inc.: Creator omnium volens genus animalium . . .   fol. 381
   Expl.: qua coctum fuerit apium. Explicit liber con-
   stantini de coitu.   fol. 384^V

   [Cf., e.g., Opera (ed. Basel, 1536), pp. 299-307.]

q) <Fragmentum experimentorum magistri Gileberti.>
   Inc.: Experimentum magistri Gileberti potentissimum
   ad maculam pannum . . .   fol. 384^V
   Expl. (mutil.): succo fenuli. rute   fol. 384^V

   [Not in Thorndike and Kibre.]

xiv c., parchment, 384 fols. In parts: (1) Fols. 1-5, single cols.
12.8 x 8.3 cms., 35 lines, written in single hand, rubr. red. (2) Fols.
6-384, double cols. 12.7 x 3.4 cms., 45 lines, written in single

hand, rubr. red and blue. Some gloses. Table of contents on inside front cover omits items a and q, and adds after item p Liber fesonomie in palma manus secundum godomum, which may thus be missing from original ms.

227 (X. 45: Pieralisi I, 308; n.a. 2312).

<Quedam summa iudicialis astronomie.>
 Inc. prol.: IN Nomine domini nostri Jhesu Christi ac
  eius beatissime matris marie . . .   fol. 1
 Inc. cap. pr.: QVum fueris interrogatus de aliqua
  re . . .   fol. 2
 Inc. cap. alt.: DVplex potest esse modus in capiendo
  ascendens hora. coniunctionis et eius horam per
  astrolabium sine radio solis . . .   fol. 2^V
 Expl.: Et he breuiter sufficiant de inueniendis Revolu-
  tionibus tam annorum mundi quam natiuitatum Et de
  ascendentibus earum. Explicit.   fol. 258

  [See Thorndike and Kibre, Suppl. II, Cum fueris . . .]

xv c., paper, [6] + 258 fols., single cols. 15.5 x 9.8 cms., 29 lines. Written in single hand. Rubr. in red and blue. At beginning 6 unnumbered fols. on different stock of paper, ruled for double cols. 14.9 x 4.7 cms., 27 lines. First unnumbered fol. has table of contents in another hand beginning Ad inueniendum ascensiones per viam Interrogationis . . .

236 (X. 54: Pieralisi I, 318-19; n.a. 805).

a) Hermannus de astrolabio.
 Inc. dedic.: HErmannus Christi pauperum peripsima et
  philosophie t<i>ronum asello immo limace tardior
  assecla .B. suo iugem in domino salutem. fol. 1
 Inc. text.: In mecienda igitur subtilissime inuencionis
  ptolomei waztalchora .i. plana spera . . . fol. 1
 Expl. (mutil.): si ad triplum subtripla. et ita in ceteris.   fol. 19^V

  [A figure follows explicit. Text contains the three
  treatises, printed as two and assigned to Hermannus
  Contractus, in B. Pez, Thesaurus anecdotorum, III.2,

94-139; and Migne, PL, CXLIII, 381 ff. Ends, incomplete, with De utilitatibus astrolabii, ii. 1 (Migne, CXLIII, 408). The treatises are now, though with doubt, assigned, respectively, to Hermannus Contractus, Gerbertus, and Hermann of Carinthia: see N. Bubnov, Gerberti opera mathematica (Berlin, 1899), pp. 109 ff.; and Haskins, Med. sci., pp. 51-53. But cf. Thorndike, vol. I, chap. xx; and Haskins, pp. 8 and 9, and nn. 20-21.]

b) Incipit liber ysagogorum alcabicii ad iudicia <translatus per Johannem Hispalensem>.

Inc. prol.: Postulata a domino prolixitate uite sceyph

eldeule .i. gladii regni . . .   fol. 20

Inc. text.: Nitac .i. zodiacus circulus signorum diuidi-

tur in .12. partes equales . . .   fol. 20^V

Expl.: perfectus. introductorius liber alcabisii. ad

magisterium iudiciorum astrorum. octauo die mensis

januarii tercie indicionis annis domini perfectis. 1181

Explicit deo gracias.   fol. 54

[See Alcabitius (ed. Venice: Melchior Sessa, 1512): (fol. 1^V) POSTULATA A DOmino prolixitate . . . : (fol. 2) NITACH idest circulus signorum: diuiditur . . . Date in explicit, obviously given according to Spanish era, is A.D. 1142. For its significance in chronology of John's works, see Thorndike, II, 74 ff., which does not, however, list present ms. and where examples mentioned are undated. Incipit of text proper varies from Thorndike and Kibre, col. 783, and otherwise not recorded there; cf. col. 430; and Carmody, Ar. astron., 27.1a.]

c) Incipit liber alfarni in .30. differentiis <scientiae astrorum. Translatus per Johannem Hispalensem>.

Inc.: NVmerus mensium arabum et latinorum est

duodenus. Menses arabum incipiunt ab almucha-

ram . . .   fol. 54

Expl.: Poterit enim pati eclipsum. in loco septentrionali.

cum distererit a cauda. per .19. gradus. et item in

meridiano antequam elongetur a cauda ultra .19.

gradus. Explicit liber alfarni. deo gracias.   fol. 84

[See Al Farghani, Differentie scientie astrorum, ed. F. J. Carmody (Berkeley, Cal., 1943); and Ar. astron., 17.1a.]

d) <Carmen de aspectibus lune ad planetas.> Sextilis aspectus lune ad solem.

Inc.: Fortunata dies ad agenda negocia regum . . .   fol. 84

Expl.: Hac nullum facies prosperitatis opus. Est aries.

    libra. taurus. scorpio. geminis Saturnus. capricornus.

    cancer. aquarius. leo. piscis. et uirgo.   fol. 87^V

    [Cf. Thorndike and Kibre, col. 270.]

e) <Duo tabulae librorum praecipue praedictionum et de
    rebus astronomicis et meteorologicis:>

    [1.] Alfraganus
        Acapicius Jo yspaniensis
        centiloquium tholomei
        aly alan rex
        quartus dictus tholomei
        liber Iudiciorum siue de medicine cordis
        messalha de interrogationibus
        Flores albumasar
        albumasar de coniunctionibus magnis
        canones de motibus planetariis
        constructio astrolabii
        ali de electionibus
        Iaffar de imbribus
        de productione radiorum

    [2.] omar de natiuitatibus
        significationes planetarum in . . . [?]
        liber de electionibus
        liber albumasaris de coniunctionibus planetarum
           ex quibus Nū sit aeris muta^i
        titulus grecatus [?] philosophi
        prophetia silbille [sic]
        interrogationes mesahale in electiones horarum etc.
        liber interrogationum mesahale
        liber [?] astrolabii

xiv c., parchment, 89 fols. Fols. 1-87 single cols. 13.6 x 10 cms.,
28 lines, written in single hand. Rubr. in red. Fols. 88 and 89
apparently added later and item e written in two hands different

70

from original scribe's. Some gloses by several contemporary hands in margins. On fol. 88 the note: <u>de diuisione zodyaci in iiii^{or} [corrected to xii] partes equales et subdiuidendo partem equalem in 30 et partem</u>. Modern vellum binding with crown and Barberini bee in gold on spine.

256 (X. 74: Pieralisi I, 340-41; n.a. 803).

<u>a</u>) Incipit liber Albumasaris in Sadam.

Inc.: <D>Ixit sadam audiui Albumasar dicentem quod
    omnis uita . . .   fol. 2

Expl.: acqua e [sic = a qua est] interrogatio. finis Ex-
    pliciunt excerpta de secretis Albumasaris per
    Sadam.   fol. 31

    [See Steinschneider (1906), 37; Thorndike, I, 651;
    <u>Isis</u>, XLV, 22-32; and Carmody, <u>Ar. astron.</u>, 13A.a;
    all of which list various mss. but not the present
    one. Fol. 1 contains table of contents.]

<u>b</u>) Opera Aly [Alhamet] Comentatoris de uniuersalibus et
    particularibus et secretis electionibus. <Liber trans-
    latus per Platonem Tiburtinum et Savasordam.>

Inc.: Rogasti me karissime ut tibi librum . . .   fol. 32

    [Cf. above, <u>MS. 182</u>, item <u>c</u>; and below, <u>MS. 328</u>,
    item <u>q</u>, and <u>335</u>, item a. Bracketed name in title
    added by another hand. Expl. fol. 60^v. Fol. 61 blank.]

<u>c</u>) Incipit epistola alchindi de Aeribus et pluuiis.

Inc.: Rogatus fui quod manifestarem . . .   fol. 62

Expl.: et corruptionem modorum suorum in secula
    seculorum amen. Explicit epistola Alchindi de Aeribus
    et pluuiis.   fol. 84

    [See Thorndike, I, 647; and Carmody, <u>Ar. astron.</u>,
    12.3a.]

<u>d</u>) Incipit liber quinquaginta preceptorum Zaelis.

Inc.: Hactenus de circuli portionibus . . .   fol. 84^v

Expl.: non parum generari signant. Explicit Liber
    .50. preceptorum Zaelis.   fol. 89

    [Evidently a different translation from above, <u>MS.</u>
    <u>155</u>; cf. Carmody, <u>Ar. astron.</u>, 3.7 and 15.3 IV.
    Fol. 89^v blank.]

e) \<Nicolai Comitis Libellus de accessu et recessu motus
   octavae spherae.\>
   Inc.: Illustri ac excelso domino domino dominico de
   malatestis. Nicolaus comes patauus plurimum se
   comissum facit. \<A\>Nimaduertente michi domine
   mi colendissime . . .   fol. 90
   Expl.: finem dicendis impono. Deo gracias.   fol. 95^V

   [In incipit a red line is drawn through Nicolaus comes.
   See Thorndike, IV, 682.]

f) Incipit liber thebit bencorath de motu octaue spere.
   Inc.: IMaginabor speram equatoris diei . . .   fol. 96
   Expl.: cum quo intrasti in linea numeri.   fol. 101^V

   [A Tabula accessionis et recessionis follows on fol.
   102. Version ascribed to Gerard of Cremona, but
   for problem of translators see Thabit b. Qurra, ed.
   Carmody (1941), p. 3; and Ar. astron., 18.1a. Cf.
   ed. Millás Vallicrosa, Estudios sobre Azarquiel
   (1943-50), pp. 494-509. Neither ed. lists present
   ms. Fol. 102^V blank.]

g) Incipit tractatus quem petrus padubanensis construxit
   in motu .8^e. spere . . .
   Inc.: QVoniam iuxta ptholomeum . . .   fol. 103
   Expl.: inde causata existent prefacti⌣ Laus deo.   fol. 114^V

   [Present ms. cited in Thorndike and Kibre, col. 597.
   Cf. Isis, XIII, 87, n. 88.]

xv c., paper, 114 fols. Written in at least five hands: (1) fols. 1-31;
(2) 32-60; (3) 62-89; (4) 90-102; (5) 103-14. Some rubr. On fol. 2,
bottom margin: Caroli Strozze Thome filii 1635.

260 (X. 78: Pieralisi I, 345; n.a. 616).\

\<Tractatus Magistri Johannis de Sacrobosco de sphaera.\>
   Inc. prooem.: Tractatum sperae quatuor capitulis dis-
   tinguimus . . .   fol. 1
   Inc. cap. 1: Descriptio sperae secundum euclidem
   SPERA est transitus . . .   fol. 1^V
   Expl.: aut deus nature patitur aut tota mundi dissoluetur
   forma et dicitur Ariopagita ab areo quod est uirtus et
   pagos quod est uilla quia ibi docebantur virtutes specu-

latiue et etiam morales; FINIS

[Present ms. not in Thorndike, Sphere of Sacrobosco (see pp. v and ix). For etymology of Ariopagita in explicit see Commentary ascribed to Michael Scot in ed. Thorndike, p. 341.]

xv c., paper, 45 fols., single cols. 12.5 x 7.9 cms., 18 lines. Written in single hand. Rubr. in red, initials of chapters in red and green. Figures in margins.

268 (X. 86: Pieralisi I, 354; n.a. 754 and VII. A. 22.).

Tractatus fratris Mathei de Aquila humilis Sacre theologie, professoris ordinis celestinorum. De causis atque natura Comete et terremotus:—

Inc.: SEpe metum post illum tremebundum . . .   fol. 1

Expl.: Fuit autem terremotus hic nonis decembris inter decimam et undecimam noctis horam ante dilucidum diei dominice et Natiuitate redentoris .1456. sub indictione quinta Imparante Regno Sicilie Serenissimo Rege Alfolso presidenteque Vniuersali Ecclesie, Serenissimo Domino Nostro Calisto Tercio:—   fol. 33

[See Thorndike, IV, 416-17; and Isis, XIII, 83, n. 65.]

xv c., paper, 33 fols., single cols. 10.7 x 6.2 cms., 14 lines. Written in single hand. Rubr. of opening title only.

270 (X. 88).

Listed by Thorndike, Isis, XIII, 68. The ms., xv c., contains Christopher de Bondelmontibus, Liber archipelagi insularum. Cf. ed. G. R. L. de Sinner (Leipzig and Berlin, 1824), p. 51: Incipit liber Insularum Archipelagi, editus per Presbyterum Christopherum de Bondelmontibus de Florentia, quem misit de civitate Rhodi Romam Domino Iordano Cardinali de Ursinis, anno Domini millesimo quadringentesimo vicesimo secundo. This ed., pp. 27-29, does not list present ms.

276 (X. 94: Pieralisi I, 365-66; n.a. <3453>).

a) <I>Ncipiunt canones azarchelis in tabulas tholetanas.' a magistro gerardo cremonensi ordinati.

Inc.: <Q>Voniam vniuscuiusque actionis quantitatem

temporis metitur spacium.' celestium motuum doc-
trinam querentibus.' eius primo ratio occurrit inuestiganda.   fol. 1

Expl.: Cuius nota. est .n.' t. autem.' est nota la —   fol. 39

[See Boncompagni, Gherardo Cremonese (Rome,
1851), p. 58; ed. Curtze, Bibl. math., 3, I (1900),
237 ff.; and Osiris, I, 766 ff. On translators and
versions see Carmody, Ar. astron., 31.1, listing
present ms. (s. n.a. 3453) under "Basic version."
Cf. below, MS. 350, item c. Fols. 39^V-40^V ruled
but blank.]

b) <C>Ompositio astrolabii.' secundum messehallach.

<Liber translatus per Johannem Hispalensem.> //
Prohemium

Inc. proh.: <S>Cito quod astrolabium est nomen
grecum . . .   fol. 41

Inc. text.: <C>Vm volueris facere astrolabium ad
cuiusque latitudinem . . .   fol. 41^V

Expl.: Post hoc extrahemus circulum capricorni.'
ex circulo arietis et libre.   fol. 50^V

[Text ends incomplete with cap. 7, followed by a
Figura inscriptionis zodiaci: see ed. Gunther, Early
science, V, 204, and fig. 64^V. Then comes the incomplete rubr. De compositione for cap. 8 (= De compositione rethis etc.). Rubr. and text continue on fol. 91:
see item f below. For this item and d and f below,
Carmody, Ar. astron., 1.1, lists present ms. (under
n.a. 2453) but with erroneous date and fols. Cf. above,
MS. 156, item f.]

c) <I>Ncipit liber <Johannis Hispalensis> de constitutione
astrolabii.

Inc.: <A>Strologice speculationis exercitium habere
volentibus. eius instrumenti ratio naturali. et quodam ordine primitus occurrit inuestiganda . . .   fol. 51

Expl.: Secundum quod exemplar.' eas in astrolabii
notabis regula. cuius hec est figura . . . <E>Xpli-
cit liber de constitutione astrolabii —   fol. 56^V

[A figure follows the words hec est figura. Cf., e.g.,
ed. Millás, Las traducciones orientales (Madrid, 1942),
pp. 316 ff.; and Carmody, Ar. astron., 37.2b. Ms. noted
in Steinschneider, Sitzungsber., CLI (1906), 59, but with

erroneous number and incipit.]

d) <I>Ncipit epilogus [sic] in usum et operationes astrolabii
   messehalle / et aliorum.

  Inc.: <N>Omina instrumentorum astrolabii sunt hec.
    Primum est armilla suspensoria ad capiendam al-
    titudinem. et dicitur arabice allahiracca . . .   fol. 57

  Expl.: Et qualis fuerit comparatio punctorum ad .12.'
    talis est comparatio stature tue / ad totam planiciem.
    <E>Xpliciunt canones de vtilitatibus et operationibus
    astrolabii. <E>Go iohannes de calomonte flandrinus
    sub anno christi .1473. currente propria manu scripsi.
    Deo gratias.   fol. 71^V

[On fol. 64^V section entitled <u>Canon docens vtilitatem
tabule regionum subscripte</u> ends: <u>representat horas
et minuta longioris diei anni</u>. Fol. 65 is ruled but
blank, and on fol. 65^V section begins entitled <u>De
ascensionibus signorum in circulo directo</u>. Cf. Gunther, <u>Early science</u>, V, 217-31; and Björnbo, <u>Bibl.
math.</u>, 2, XII, 195 and 199. Ms. noted in Steinschneider, <u>Sitzungsber.</u>, CLI (1906), 59; and Carmody, <u>Ar.
astron.</u>, 1.1 (s. n.a. 3453). Cf. below, <u>MS. 303</u>, item <u>i</u>.]

e) <I>Ncipit tractatus quadrantis.

  Inc. pars prima: <G>Eometrie due sunt partes. theorica
    .s. [<u>sup. lin. add. corrector</u>] et practica. Practica
    est.' que sola mentis speculatione . . .   fol. 72

  Expl. pars prima: Et margarita perforata moueatur
    super filum de loco ad locum. Et erit completa
    compositio quadrantis.   fol. 77

  <P>Ars secunda. De vtilitatibus et operationibus quad-
    rantis // De altitudinem solis inuenienda.

  Inc. pars prima partis secundae: <D>Icto de composi-
    tione quadrantis. Dicendum est de utilitatibus et
    operationibus.' que habentur per eum. <S>I igitur
    uelis scire altitudinem solis in omni hora per quad-
    rantem . . .   fol. 78

  De mensuratione plani. Que est secunda pars.

  Inc. pars secunda partis secundae: <S>ecunda pars men-
    surandi huius doctrine. que est planimetria. habet duas
    partes . . .   fol. 86

<u>Expl.</u>: <S>I autem fuerit   fol. 87^V

[Text ends thus, incomplete, at bottom of fol. 87^V
with opening words of section entitled <u>De mensura-</u>
<u>tione scalenonis superficie</u>. Fols. 88-90^V ruled but
blank. See ed. Tannery, <u>Notices et extraits des mss.</u>
<u>de la Bibl. Nat.</u>, XXXV (1896), 561-632, and <u>Isis,</u>
XXXIV, 467-69, which do not, however, list present
ms. Ascribed by Tannery to 'Robertus Anglicus in
Montepessulano,' but for problem of authorship,
whether Robertus Anglicus, John of Montpellier, or
another, see Thorndike in <u>Isis</u>, XXXVII, 150-53.]

<u>f)</u> <Continuatio compositionis astrolabii secundum Messehallam
translatae per Johannem Hispalensem.>

<u>Inc. cap. 8</u>: <E>T post constitutionem horum trium cir-
culorum. scilicet capricorni. et arietis et libre. ac
cancri. fac circulum signorum . . .   fol. 91

<u>Expl.</u>: Et nota illa.' erit polus zodiaci. vt patet in
figura . . . <E>Xplicit compositio astrolabii.   fol. 109

[A figure follows the words <u>vt patet in figura</u>. Fols.
109^V-110^V ruled but blank. Text preceded on fol. 91
by rubr. words <u>rethis.' Et primo de inscriptione</u>
<u>zodiaci</u>, i.e. remnant of title to cap. 8: see above,
item <u>b</u> and note; and Gunther, <u>Early science</u>, V,
204 ff.]

<u>g)</u> <Tractatus anonymi de practica astrolabii.>

<u>Inc.</u>: <Q>antum ad partem primam.' antequam procedo
ad practicam huius instrumenti.' premitto propter
minus peritos in calculatione et modo procedendi in
astrologia . . .   fol. 111

<u>Expl.</u>: cum annis distantibus ab anno compositionis
instrumenti.   fol. 124^V

[Tables follow on fols. 125-27. Fols. 127^V-29 ruled
but blank.]

xv c., paper, 129 fols. Made up of two parts: (1) Fols. 1-110,
single cols. 15.3 x 9.7 cms., 32 lines, on single stock of paper
having as water mark crossbow enclosed in an ellipse. Rubr.,
tables and figures in black and red. Written in 1473 by Johannes
de Calomonte Flandrinus (see explicit of item <u>d</u>), professor at
Perugia and author of <u>Alfonsi regis tabule</u> . . . <u>cum additionibus</u>
(A.D. 1467): see <u>MS. Vat. lat. 8951</u>; and <u>Isis</u>, XIII, 93. In present

instance he is not only scribe but editor and commentator, illustrating his texts from other versions and gloses and occasionally adding materials of his own. Thus for Azarchel (item <u>a</u>) he frequently gives variant readings in the marg., beginning them <u>In alio erat sic</u> (e.g. fols. 12, 20^V, 31^V). For Messahala (item <u>b</u>), among numerous comments, see fol. 48, marg.: <u>Ego iohannes de calomonte. / Ista littera id est super .e. cuspidem erectis angulis. rarissime inuenitur in exemplaribus nisi forte tamquam glosa. uel tamquam littera alterius positionis.</u> (Cf. fol. 49^V, marg.). Similar notes occur for item <u>d</u> on, e.g., fols. 57, 58^V, 59^V, 60^V, 61, 62^V, 68, 71^V. Further evidence of his editorial activities appears in comments on added chapters in the version of Messahala represented by item <u>d</u>. Thus, fol. 60, Johannes writes: <u>hoc capitulum. Si per allidadam. et capitulum subsequens. Item per alidadam / sunt ambo addita:</u> see Gunther, V, 220-21, chaps. 11 and 12. Cf. also the marg. of fols. 61, 61^V, 62^V, 66^V, etc. And on fol. 64, at the title <u>Canon docens vtilitatem tabule regionum subscripte</u> he writes: <u>Hanc litteram ego iohannes de calomonte cum sua tabula immediate subscripta adidi.</u> For the <u>Tractatus quadrantis</u> (item <u>e</u>) see fol. 87, marg.: <u>Ego iohannes de calomonte. Pauca exempla habent hanc litteram Et linea iacens intelligatur erecta.</u> Similar notes occur for item <u>f</u>, and there are other gloses throughout, explaining passages, clarifying readings, and offering alternate measuring methods. (2) Fols. 111-27, single cols. 15 x 12 cms., 30 lines, on single stock of paper having as watermark cardinal's hat (see above, <u>MS. 156</u>, part (1)). Spaces for rubr. initials and, fol. 116^V, for table or figure, but none executed. Written in single hand different from (1). Originally fols. 91-110 followed fol. 50 but have become displaced, and the n.a. 3453 (as recorded in Pieralisi) has disappeared, apparently in rebinding. Contents of ms. listed, but quite inaccurately, by Steinschneider, <u>Bullettino</u>, XX(1887), 12-13 and n. 2.

77 (X. 95: Pieralisi I, 367; n.a. 787).

A miscellany of texts in veterinary medicine, of which one is
    in Latin:
    <Hippiatria sive Marescalia Laurentii Rusii.>
    <u>Inc. cap. I</u>: De natura equorum. Equus callide nature
        consideratur . . .   fol. 1

<u>Inc. cap. II</u>: De electione parentum equorum. QVoniam omne

animal consueuit sibi simile generare . . .   fol. 1

<u>Inc. cap. III</u>: Quot sunt spectanda in parentibus equorum.

QVatuor in parentibus spectanda sunt . . .   fol. 1

<u>Expl.</u>: et fac omne simul bullire et fac Vnguentum et

Vnge. et cetera. Deo gratias amen. Tελωc.   fol. 100

> [A Latin rendering of a work originally written in
> the vernacular: see E. Narducci, "Il trattato di mas-
> calcia di Lorenzo Rusio scritto nel secolo xiii in
> vernacolo romano," <u>Rendiconti Accad. Lincei</u>, Cl.
> sc. mor., stor., filol., Ser. V, 1 (1892), 432-34; and
> ed. Lutetiae: C. Wechelus, 1532; and ed. P. Delprato
> and L. Barbieri (Coll. d. opere ined. o rare, vols.
> XIX and XX, Bologna, 1867-70). Present ms., which
> lacks title and the dedication <u>Laurentii ad N. sancti
> Hadriani diaconum cardinalem</u>, is unknown to Delprato
> and Barbieri and to Narducci. Incipit not listed in
> Thorndike and Kibre; but see col. 361.]

xv c., paper, [8] + 103 fols., single cols. 15.3 x 10 cms., varying
25 and 26 lines. Written in single hand. Rubr. in red. Fols. 100-103
contain various recipes in Italian written in several later hands.
Preceding fol. 1 eight leaves have been added from a different
stock of paper, on first five of which a more recent hand has written
a table of contents by chapters of the work which follows. Binding
modern vellum with Barberini bee stamped in gold on spine.

279 (X. 97: Pieralisi I, 369; n.a. 769 and VII. B. 11).

Ad Reuerendum in Christo patrem et dominum dominum

Astorgium Agnensem beneuentanum Archiepiscopum

Marchie Anchonitane Gubernatorem Benedictus re-

guardatus Nursinus phisicus de Conseruanda Sanitatem.

<u>Inc.</u>: SVMMO cum Studio decet emergentes morborum

insidias . . .   fol. 1

<u>Expl.</u>: ad sanitatis conseruationem iuuamentum pre-

stat.   fol. 87[V]

> [See <u>Isis</u>, XIII, 63, § 18, and n. 53; and Giacosa,
> <u>Mag. salern.</u>, p. 433.]

xv c., paper, [3] + 87 fols., single cols. 14.3 x 8 cms., 27 lines.
Written in single hand. Rubr. in red, and initial on fol. 1 illuminated
in red, green, blue, yellow and gold. On lower marg. of fol. 1 a coat

of arms: cross with four small circles, all on a shield, and the
initials B and F. Three blank sheets, of same stock of paper as
the rest, precede fol. 1, which is in modern numbering. On first
two of these sheets a different hand writes a table of contents and
the date 1474. Various notes of ownership, including the date 1633.
On fol. 87: Joannis Baptiste Ciarlini Carpm̃.

283 (X. 101 and 1718: Pieralisi I, 373; n.a. 1763).

a) Didascalicon Hugonis de Sancto Victore.
  Inc. praef. pr.: Tribus modis res subsistere habent. In
    actu. In intellectu. In mente diuina . . .   fol. 1
  Inc. praef. alt.: Multi sunt quos ipsa a domino [sic]
    natura ingenio . . .   fol. 1
  Expl.: unus spiritus cum ipso animo uoluntario studuerimus
    in mandatis eius perseuerare. Explicit Liber didascali-
    con magistri Hugonis de Sancto Victore.   fol. 36

  [Contains preface characteristic of δ family of mss.;
  cf. ed. Buttimer (1929), pp. xxxi and 134-35. Title and
  last sentence of explicit in later hand.]

b) Anonymi Episcopi Tractatus de musica.
  Inc.: Desiderio tuo fili karissime gratuito conscenderem:
    si rationi preuie . . .   fol. 37
    Creatrix omnium sapientia. creaturas omnes fecit. in
    numero. pondere et mensura . . .   fol. 37^V
  Expl.: longe plenius armonia celestium cum cognita fuerit.
    eorum archana consilia reuelabunt.   fol. 42^V

  [Title in a later hand. Not in Coussemaker, Script.
  de mus. med. aev., nor Gerbert, Script. eccles. de
  musica; and not in Thorndike and Kibre.]

c) Anonymi Compendiosus tractatus de philosophia et eius
    secretis.
  Inc. prol.: <G>loria deo principio sine principio, fini sine
    fine. qui fuit ante omnia. et erit post omnia eter-
    nus . . .   fol. 45
  Inc. part. I: Diffinitio philosophie. Philosophia est igitur
    amor. et studium sapientie . . .   fol. 45
  Inc. part. II: . . . incipit secunda que continet quomodo
    elementa facta sunt . . .Superius diximus quod . . . fol. 61^V

Inc. part. III: . . . incipit tercia que continet capitulum.

de humoribus . . . <P>hilosophia ueraciter tenet . . .fol. 74

Expl. part. V: Ibi quoque longissima dies usque ad horas

.x. et vii. fol. 106^V

[Incipit of prologue in Thorndike and Kibre, cols.
279 and 269, under Alcantarus Caldeorum; see also
Björnbo, Bibl. math., 3, XII, 206. But present tractate is a different work, addressed to Robertus can-
cellarius regis ytalie (fol. 66^V), "anti-Salernitan"
in its account of the elements (see Mediaeval studies,
XVI, 162), though drawing on similar sources—Constantinus Afer, Johannitius, Ypocras de humana
natura, etc. Title written in later hand.]

d) <Anonymi Glosulae de saporibus, etc.>

Inc. pr.: In prima huius capituli dicitur quod duo sunt

sapores initiales potentissimus scilicet et insipidus.

ex quibus alii extrahuntur sapores . . . fol. 106^V

Expl. pr.: In fructu enim procere arboris proprie [?]

longitudinem coagulatur [?] . . . fol. 110

Inc. alt.: fructus non sunt in parte . . . fol. 110

Expl. alt.: Silurens uero nascentes in locis siccis diffi-

cilius mutauimus [?] sed facilius coagulatur humecta

pars. fol. 116^V

[Not in Thorndike and Kibre.]

xiii-xv c., parchment, 116 fols., originally three separate mss.:
(1) Fols. 1-36, xiii/xiv c., single col. 18 x 8 cms., 34 lines, and
17.6 x 10.3 cms., 35 lines. Written in two contemporary hands.
No rubr. (2) Fols. 37-44, xiv c., smaller leaves, double cols. 12.4 x
4 cms., 27 lines. Written in single hand, smaller than those of ms.
1. Rubr. in red and blue, with ornamented initial on fol. 37 in red,
blue, apricot, and gold. Fols. 43-44 blank. (3) Fols. 45-116, xiv c.,
single col. 16.3 x 9.6 cms., 39 lines. Item c written in a single
hand larger than that of ms. 2 but smaller than those of 1. Item d
written in two later hands (xv c. ?). Rubr. in red. A more recent
hand has written titles and explicits to items a, b, and c. On fol. 1,
lower margin: Caroli Strozze Thome filii. On fol. 1, upper outside
margin, a modern hand writes a table of contents, listing items a,
b, and c only.

296 (X. 114: Pieralisi I, 387; n.a. 798 and VII. C. 5).

a) Canones in tabulas planetarum, et subiunguntur ipsae
   tabulae planetarum Alfonsinae.

Inc. text.: In nomine domini scitote quod annus lunaris
   sit ex ccc. l.iiii^{or}. diebus et quinta et sexta diei
   parte . . .   fol. 1

Inc. cap. de scientia introitus mensium arabum: arabum
   accipitur annos arabum perfectos . . .   fol. 1

Inc. cap. de scientia capitis mensium arabum: Cvm
   uolueris radix adde super radicem . . .   fol. 1

Expl.: Cauendum autem ut hore supradicte secundum
   s. . . plent. [?] regionis accipiantur.   fol. 10^{V}

[Tables follow in black and red through fol. 54^{V}, but
52^{V} is blank and 53^{rv} contains different tables and text
as noted in item b below. Cf. Thorndike and Kibre, col.
651 (s. Scito quod annus); and Carmody, Ar. astron.,
31.1d; both under Azarchel (Arzachel), or Abredele
or Abrelliele.]

b) <Fragmenta tabularum et canonum aliorum.>

Inc.: Si pasca iudeorum uolueris inuestigare . . .Numerus
   dierum mensium in anno ordinato sic disponere . . .fol. 53^{rv}

[Tables occur on same fol. Incipit not listed in
Thorndike and Kibre.]

xv c., parchment, to which are added 8 leaves of paper, 62 fols.
Item a written single cols. and in a single hand. Same hand writes
title in marg. of fol. 1: Canones ad tabulas planetarum. Item b
written in another hand. Insides of both covers have further notes
on time reckoning in various hands. On front cover, inside: Anno
domini 1298 motus .g. sp . . . 6 in ♄. 9.6.4 addet mensurarum.
Ownership note, fol. 1, bottom marg.: Caroli Strozzę Thomę filii
1695.

02 (X. 120: Pieralisi I, 394; n.a. 748 and 72).

a) <Ursonis Aphorismi cum Glosulis eiusdem.>
Inc.: Cum phisicalis scientie inuentores aut negligencia
   tediosi aut ignorancia . . .   fol. 1
Expl.: Idcirco datori numerum gracias reddite cui est
   honor et gloria laus et potestas in secula seculorum.

Amen. Expliciunt Glosule aphorismorum Vrsonis ad eodem Iuuente [et de qualitatum commistionibus].   fol. 19^V

[The added words in square brackets of the explicit are in another hand. Ms. listed in Thorndike and Kibre, col. 649, but with Pieralisi's erroneous incipit and erroneous author's name; cf. cols. 118 and 601. Commentary varies from that printed in Rudolf Creutz, Die Medizinisch-Naturphilosophischen Aphorismen und Kommentare des Magister Urso Salernitanus (Quellen u. Stud. zur Gesch. d. Naturwissensch. u. d. Mediz., dir. Diepgen u. Ruska, Band V. 1, Berlin, 1936), esp. pp. 10-130, which does not list present ms.]

<u>b</u>) Incipit liber <anonymi> de commistionibus elementorum
    [et compositione eorum.]

    <u>Inc.</u>: Cum medicinalis sciencia ceteris elegantior et
      utilior in theorica et practica auctorum communi
      testimonio diuidatur . . .   fol. 20

    <u>Expl.</u>: Licet confusione . . . declarari non possint quia
      uarietates saporum et per naturam in diuersis.   fol. 39^V

    [The added words in square brackets at the end of the title are in another hand. Incipit not listed in Thorndike and Kibre.]

xiv c., parchment, 39 fols., double cols. 19.9 x 6 cms., 59 lines. Written in single hand. Rubr. in red and blue. Note on fol. 39^V, bottom margin: <u>Caribertii .72</u>, in same hand as that of n.a. 72 on fol. 1.

303 (X. 121: Pieralisi I, 395-97; n.a. 797 and VII. C. 4.).

    <u>a</u>) <Fragmentum astronomicum.> V.^{a} tabula. Tabula
      declinationis solis ab equinoctiali . . . Isti sunt anni
      arabum quibus astrologi utuntur in ratione lune.

    <u>Inc. text.</u>: CUrrente anno domini .1255. die lune .9.
      intrante . . .   fol. 1^V

    <u>Expl.</u>: quia in .30. annis sunt et complentur undecim
      anni lune bisexales.   fol. 1^V

    [Begins, incomplete, with a table of the sun's declination.]

    <u>b</u>) <Collectus capitulorum de rebus astronomicis et mete-
      orologicis.>

    Incipit 2.^{a} particula candele <carminis>. de equatoribus

planetarum:-

Inc. carm.: Qualiter in celo sedeant tunc sydera scito. fol. 2

Expl. carm.: Ordo rei. Racioque rei. bene rem facit
esse. fol. 2^V

<Incipit> De statione vel retrogradatione planetarum . . . fol. 2^V

<Incipit> Tractatus ad pronosticandum qualitates
temporis uenturas. fol. 5

<Incipit> Differentia .7^a in proprietate diuisionum
quarte partis habitabilis . . .

Inc.: Nunc narremus proprietates locorum . . . fol. 5

Expl.: fractiones diuidentes a distanta diuidendis:- fol. 6^V

[A miscellany of various sources, written continuously
as if a single work though with differentiating rubrics;
i.e. the opening fragment is of an astronomical poem,
the rest is prose; Differentia .7^a is drawn from Alfraganus, Differentie scientie astrorum (cf. ed. Carmody,
pp. 11 ff.); etc. A table follows text, fol. 6^V; and on
fols. 7-8^V are astronomical figures in another hand.]

c) Incipit theorica planetarum ex figuris circulorum
eorundem . . .

Inc.: Circulus excentricus dicitur uel egresse cus-
pidis . . . fol. 9

Expl.: ut aut maioris quantitatis. Explicit Deo gratias. fol. 12

[Ascribed in other mss. variously to Gerard of
Cremona, Gerard of Sabbioneta, Walter Britte,
Simon Bredon, John of Spain. Cf. ed. Carmody
(1942); Ar. astron., 36.1; and Thorndike and
Kibre, col. 102.]

d) Incipit tractatus de semisse. Magistri petri de sancto
amato.

Inc.: QUoniam non conceditur nobis philosophie . . . fol. 12

[See Thorndike and Kibre, cols. 599 and 589, s.n.
Petrus de S. Audomaro. Following text are tables,
fols. 16^V-17^V.]

e) Incipit prohemium glossarum canonum <Johannis de
Sicilia> super Tabulas toletanas <Azarchelis sive
Al-Zarkali>.

Inc.: Inter cetera ueritatis phylosophice . . . fol. 18

Expl: stellam oriri de nocte. fol. 67

> [Cf. Bibl. math., 3, XII, 115; and Osiris, I, 772.
> Table of contents follows this work on fol. 67-67^V.
> Fol. 67^V, col. 2-68^V originally blank. On fol. 69 is
> a brief passage on meteorology beginning, frag-
> mentarily, humidum et uentosam fore significat.
> Si sol rubeat fortasse . . . (=Albumasar?).]

f) Incipiunt flores Albumasar quos collegit ex dictis suis. . .

    Inc.: DIxit albumasar. Oportet te primo scire . . .   fol. 69

    Expl.: Et ipse est auxiliator. Explicit. Expliciunt flores

    albumasar cum laude de<i>.   fol. 73^V

> [See, e.g., ed. Venice: Sessa, 1500 [?]; and Carmody,
> Ar. astron., 13.3a. Cf. above, MS. 182, item h.]

g) Incipit liber de coniunctione et receptione. et de inter-
    rogationibus. a messahala astrologo editus.

    Inc.: CUm reges antiquos quorum peritia . . .   fol. 74

    Expl.: et die econtrario scilicet pro bono malum:-
    Explicit.   fol. 79^V

> [Not in Thorndike and Kibre; and differs from
> Carmody, Ar. astron., 1.3a.]

h) Incipit liber alboaly de natiuitate quidquid agunt planete
    in signis et domibus planetarum. De saturno.

    Inc.: SAturnus cum fuerit in domo suo . . .   fol. 79^V

    Expl.: Si fuerit in domo lune infirmitatem . . . dissipare

    figure.   fol. 79^V

> [Incipit not in Thorndike and Kibre for versions by
> John of Spain or Plato of Tivoli: cf. cols. 208, 211,
> 370.]

i) Incipit liber <Messahala> de operatione astralabii. De
    nominibus.

    Inc.: NOmina instrumentorum astralabii sunt hec . . . fol. 79^V

    Expl.: et equalis fiat comparata stature tue ad totam
    planitiem. Explicit liber de operatione astralabii.   fol. 81

> [See above, MS. 276, item d. A table follows text on
> fol. 81^V.]

j) Incipit tractatus de impressionibus aeris / breuiter com-
    positus secundum sententiam aristotelis in libro me-

thaurorum.

Inc.: EOrum que generantur quedam generantur in sub-

limi . . .   fol. 82

Inc. cap. penult.: De augmento et decremento maris

. . .   fol. 83^V

Inc. cap. ult.: De Hiis que sunt in superiori regione

. . .   fol. 83^V

Expl. (part. illeg.): solem et alios pl' [?] . . .   fol. 83^V

[Evidently the same work as that attributed in Vat.
MS. Ottob. lat. 1814, fol. 54 to a Magister Sturio
(Sturius); see Pelster, Philos. Jahrbuch, XXXVI,
154-55.]

k) Incipit liber de aspectibus lune cum planetis. Prologus.

Inc.: IN nomine misericordis et pii dei. Dixit. Postquam

inspexi electiones lunares . . .   fol. 83^V

Expl. (part. illeg.): sed capricornus magis tendit ad

frigus . . . hiis opponitur id est cancer et leo . . .

et sagitarius . . .   fol. 87^V

[On fol. 87, col. 1, introitus bal. quies et solitudo.
Perfectus est liber cum laude dei; but this is followed, col. 2, by a passage beginning Cum luna
fuerit cum capite uel cauda in uno signo, and on
fol. 87^V, col. 1, by Quando sol fuerit in emisperio
australi, which seem to be parts of the same work.
Present ms. cited in Thorndike and Kibre, col. 330;
but Carmody, Ar. astron., 1.7a, erroneously lists
this item as being Messahala, De rebus eclipsium:
see MS. 328, item i, below. On fol. 87^V, col. 2, a
note in a later hand begins Pestes et bubones et
humiditas.]

l) Incipit liber <pseudo-Aristotilis> de significationibus

aquarum et uentorum. et tempestatum et serenitatum.

<non, ut videtur, Bartholomaei de Messana, sed

secundum aliam quamdam translationem.>

Inc.: SIgna aquarum. et uentorum et tempestatum . . .

Que quidem nos ipsi perspeximus. et que . . .

accepimus . . . matutinales . . .   fol. 88

Expl.: sed aut ante ipsam aut apparet postea. Explicit. fol. 89^V

[A complete text of the variant translation otherwise
fragmentarily preserved in Oxford MS. Corp. Chr.
243 (xv c.), fols. 52-53, which breaks off near begin-

ning in sec. De signis pluuie with words aves qui vivunt in insula aquam signant. Cf. above, MS. 165, item 36; and see Lacombe, I, 409. Present ms. not in Lacombe, II, 1162-64; and version not in Thorndike and Kibre.]

m) Incipit regula abenahar de temporibus pluuiarum:-

Inc.: QUotiens de pluuiis earumque statu. et de aeris mutatione . . . fol. 89^V

Expl.: si deinceps stellis inferioribus. Explicit quod inueni de summa tractatus pluuiarum Harbernahar. fol. 90

[See Ja 'far Indus, De mutatione temporis, caps. 3-6, init. (unnumbered), in Astrorum iudices Alkindus [et] Gaphar de pluuiis imbribus et ventis: ac aeris mutatione (Venice: Liechtenstein, 1507), sigs. C$_2$^{r}, col. 2-[C$_4$^{r}], col. 1. Cf. Carmody, Ar. astron., 12A, 1.I, cap. 4. Not in Thorndike and Kibre.]

n) Incipit doctrina lipuldi ad precognoscendas pluuias.

Inc.: AD precognoscendum aeris mutationem magister lipuldus extraxit . . . fol. 90

Expl. (mutil.): parum ad austrum et parum ad aquilonem tempestatem . . . fol. 90^V

[Incipit not in Thorndike and Kibre; but cf. col. 178. For Leopoldus on meteorology see Hellmann, Beiträge z. Gesch. d. Meteor., II, 176-79.]

xiii c. [?], parchment, 92 fols. (numbered 1-92, and unnumbered fol. following 7 marked 7a in pencil). Chief texts written in at least two hands: (1) Fols. 1-68, double cols. 16 x 7 cms., 58 lines and varying; but fols. 9-10^V and 11^V single cols.; and fol. 1^V, col. 1 ruled 75 lines (measurements uncertain from destruction of lower marg.). (2) Fols. 69-91, double cols. 17.5 x 6.5 cms., 54 lines. Rubr. red and blue, initials ornamented in red, blue, violet, and gold. Gloses and notes in various hands in marg.; and on fols. 67, 68 and 91, which were originally blank. Original leaves evidently missing at beginning and before fols. 2, 69 and 82; and throughout injury to bottom marg. has affected text. On paper fly leaf table of contents in modern hand. On fol. 1, top inner marg. the date 1453; bottom marg. Caroli Strozze Thome filii 1635.

305 (X. 123: Pieralisi I, 400; n.a. 761).

<Michaelis Scoti Abbreviatio Avicennae Libri animalium cum

Dedicatione Henrici Coloniensis.>

Inc. dedic.: Frederice romanorum imperator domine
   mundi suscipe deuoto hunc laborem michaelis
   scoti . . .   fol. 1

Inc. text.: <U>t animalium quidam . . .   fol. 1

Expl.: iam scis ex alio loco. Completus est liber auicenne
   de animalibus scriptus per magistrum henricum colo-
   niensem ad exemplar magnifici in primis domini fre-
   derici apud messi<n>am ciuitatem apulie ubi dictus
   imperator eidem magistro henrico librum promissum
   acomodauit. anno domini .m^o.cc^o.xxxii^o. in uigilia
   beati laurencii. et cetera.   fol. 49^V

[For confirmation and importance of date in explicit,
correcting Vatican MS. lat. 4428, which reads MCC
etc., see J. L. A. Huillard-Bréholles, Historia diplo-
matica Friderici Secundi (Paris, 1859-61), IV, 381;
and Haskins, Med. sci., pp. 273 and 279. Ms. noted
in Thorndike and Kibre, col. 741, and Lacombe, II,
1164. Cf. Isis, XIII, 83, § 65, and n. 66.]

xiii c., parchment, 49 fols., double cols. 17.6 x 5 cms., 50 lines.
Written in single hand. Rubr. in red. Some gloses in margins. On
two fols. bound in at front a fragment of Liber reg. (ix c.).

306 (X. 124).

Listed by Thorndike, III, 527-34, and in Isis, XIII, 92. The ms.
   contains William de Marra of Padua, Sertum papale de
   venenis, written for Pope Urban V.

307 (X. 125: Pieralisi I, 402-4; n.a. 841 and VII. D. 18.).

a) <Magistri Johannis Veruli de Anagnia Liber de arte
     musicae.>

Inc.: Cum igitur de arte musice tractare debeamus. Primo
   uidendum est quid sit musica . . .   fol. 1

Expl.: et quando prolatio minor miscitur cum maiore aut
   minima prolatio cum minore. Finito Libro Sit Laus
   gloria Christo . . . Explicit liber de musica magistri
   Iohannis ueruli de anagnia.   fol. 16^V

[See Coussemaker, Script. de mus. med. aev., III,
129-77.]

<u>b</u>) <Philippi de Vitriaco Ars nova.>

<u>Inc.</u>: Musice tria sunt genera mundanum humanum et
   instrumentale. de instrumentali ad presens est intentio
   vnde musica instrumentalis dicitur . . . fol. 17

<u>Expl.</u>: Et est notandum quod maius tempus imperfectum
   se habet sicut maius tempus perfectum. Explicit ars
   noua magistri Philippi de Uetri Deo gratias Amen.
   Amen. Amen. fol. 20^{V}

[See Coussemaker, III, 13-22.]

<u>c</u>) <Theodoni de Caprio Liber de musica mensurabili.>

<u>Inc.</u>: Omnis ars siue doctrina honorabiliorem . . . fol. 21

<u>Expl.</u>: quod ueterat idem. fol. 27

[Ascribed to Theodoricus de Campo in Coussemaker,
III, 177-93, and Thorndike and Kibre, col. 465; but see
R. Casimiri, <u>Note d'archivio per la storia musicale</u>,
XIX, 38-41 and 93-98.]

<u>d</u>) Incipit capitulum de musica .I. <Isidori hispalensis>.

<u>Inc.</u>: Mvsica est peritia modulationis sono cantuque
   consistens . . . fol. 27

<u>Expl.</u>: eleuatione et positione. fol. 29

[<u>Etymologiae</u>, III, xv-xxiii. Thorndike and Kibre,
col. 421, lists incipit for Regino, <u>De plana musica</u>,
but not for Isidore. See explicit and note in next
item.]

<u>e</u>) <Gregorii praesulis Capitulum> De .viii^{o}. tonis.

<u>Inc. prol.</u>: Gregorius presul meritis et nomine dignus
   vnde genus duxit summum conscendit honorem Re-
   nouauit monumenta patrum Tunc composuit hunc librum seu libellum musice artis scole cantorum . . .fol. 29

<u>Inc.</u>: De autentico protho. Autentus protus habet plures
   uarietates denique introitum . . . fol. 29

<u>Expl.</u>: nec sursum nec infra nisi puncta aut duo aut .iii.
   aut .v. faciunt neomam. Explicit tractatus de musica
   beati Ysodori Yspalensis episcopi [<u>sic</u>]. fol. 29

[Item <u>e</u> written continuously with <u>d</u> as if part of
Isidore, hence not in Casimiri. Not in Thorndike
and Kibre.]

f) <Fragmentum de novem musis.>

    Inc.: Ut superius dictum est permultos nouem sunt muse.
       et dicitur secundum fabulas habitare in monte elycone
       prima dicitur clio . . .   fol. 29

    Expl.: Nonum est quod eligis bene proferre. hic est ordo
       sapientie.   fol. 29

    [Not in Thorndike and Kibre.]

g) Ars et modus pulsandi organa secundum modum nouissi-
    mum inuentum per magistros modernos.

    Inc.: Nota quod omnes uoces totius organi tam toni quam
       semitoni possint esse . . .   fol. 29$^\mathrm{V}$

    Expl.: Iste sunt bone seste .C.A. D.B. C[sic = E]. semi-
       totonum [sic]. qui est inter C. et D. F. et D. G.E. A
       semitonum qui est inter F. et G. B. semitonum qui
       est inter .G. et .A.   fol. 30

    [Ed. Casimiri, pp. 100-101. Not in Thorndike and Kibre.]

h) Incipiunt Regule contrapuncti ordinate per Venerabilem
    virum fratrem Theodonum de Caprio de Ciuitate sante
    Agathes priorem Capuanum ordinis Sacri monasterii
    montis uirginis In anno domini 1431. none Indictionis
    .13$^\mathrm{o}$ mensis Iulii et In primis ostendendum est que et
    quot sunt consonantie tam perfecte quam Inperfecte.
    secundum naturam hominis.

    Inc.: Item sciendum est quot sunt species biscanti . . . fol. 30

    Expl.: post eas'simplices consonantias componendo
       etc.   fol. 31$^\mathrm{V}$

    [A tabular summary, written in red, appears at the
    bottom of fol. 30$^\mathrm{V}$, Inc.: Nota quod regula generalis
    est quando volumus canere per octauam semper de
    omne vt octaua est fa . . . Ed. Casimiri, pp. 94-98.
    Not in Thorndike and Kibre.]

i) Incipiunt Capitula de proportionibus. in primis uidendum
    est de tono et quare dicitur tonus et in quo proportione
    consistit et quare dicitur sex q.8.

    Inc.: Sexquioctaua proporcio est quoniam maior numerus
       continet totum minorem numerum . . .   fol. 31$^\mathrm{V}$

89

Expl.: Sexta est geometria que loquitur de mensuris.
Septima est astronomia que loquitur de celo et planetis
celi et cursum stellarum . . . Circuli celorum nomina
hec sunt. Luna. Mercurius. Venus. sol. Mars. Iouis
Saturnus. Terra spera celestis.   fol. 31^V

[Omitted in Casimiri's account of ms. Not in Thorndike
and Kibre.]

j) Incipit ars magistri Johannis de muris de francia scripta
per venerabilem virum et religiosum fratrem theodo-
num de sancta Agatha priorem Capuanum ordinis sacri
monasterii montis uirginis. Sub anno domini 1432.
Vltimo mensis marcii decime Indictionis . . .

Inc.: Mvsica est artium domina. continens omnium metho-
dorum principia . . .   fol. 31^V

Expl. (mutil.): In perfectam siue mino: fol. 31^V

[Ends incomplete. Not in Coussemaker or Gerbert,
Script. eccles. de musica. Not in Thorndike and
Kibre.]

xv c., parchment, 32 fols., double cols., written in various hands,
as follows: (1) Fols. 1-16^V, 19.2 x 6.3 cms., 43 lines. (2) Fols. 17-
29^V, 18.9 x 16.3 cms., 40 lines. (3) Fols. 29^V-30, 18 x 6.4 cms., 34
lines. (4) Fols. 30-30^V, varying 19 to 24 cms. x 7.7 cms., 30-47
lines. (5) Fols. 31-31^V, 18.3 x 7 cms., 41 lines. (6) Fol. 31^V, 21.4 x
8 cms., 43 lines. Rubr. in red, blue, purple, and green. Fols. 1-17
elaborately illuminated and with ornamental borders; illum. initial
on fol. 21. Ms. originally had 40 or more fols., as evidenced from
older fol. numberings in red; but fols. 17-24 were early removed.
The missing fols. contained works by Imbertus de Grancia and
perhaps Johannes de Muris, from indications in table of contents
(xviiith c.) on the fly leaf. At the beginning of item c (fol. 21, upper
right margin) another hand than the scribe's has written: Alius
auctor ex multis auctoribus, and at its end (fol. 27): sine nomine
auctoris. ab Omnis ars. sed. accepit ab aliis.

309 (X. 127: Pieralisi I, 406-7; n.a. 667 and 740, and VII. A. 10.).

A collection of commentaries on Aristotle by Aegidius Romanus,
Thomas Aquinas, Petrus de Alvernia and William of Spain,

of which these, chiefly on the Parva naturalia, are relevant
to the present catalogue:

a) <Liber Thomae Aquinatis de sensu et sensato.>

Inc.: Sicut philosophus dicit in tercio de anima . . .   fol. 19

Expl.: et in sompniis fit aliqua precognitio futurorum

explicit de sensu et sensato.   fol. 7^V

[The folios containing this text, which are disarranged
throughout, must be read in the following order: 19, 17,
13, 15, 11, 9, 10, 12, 16, 14, 18, 20, 2-7; and a part of
the text (lect. XV, § 219, ad init., to lect. XVII, § 259,
ad fin., ed. Spiazzi [Marietti, 1949]) is evidently missing.
See next item below.]

b) Incipit <Liber Thomae Aquinatis> de memoria et reminis-

centia. <Fragmentum.>

Inc.: SIcut philosophus dicit in .vii^o. de historiis animali-

um . . .   fol. 7^V

Expl. (mutil.): Deinde cum dicit. sunt autem et superi fol. 8^V

[Evidently once complete, the present remnant, in two
displaced folios, contains only half the opening section
(lect. I, § 298, ed. Spiazzi) and the whole or part of 23
later sections (lect. VI, § 384, ad fin., to lect. VIII, § 406,
ad init.).]

c) <Liber Petri de Alvernia de somno et vigilia.>

Inc.: SEcundum philosophum secundo phisicorum Quecum-

que . . .   fol. 25

Expl.: supernaturali deo qui est benedictus in secula secu-

lorum. ¶Hec est expositio Magistri .p. de aluernia su-

per libro aristotelis de sompno et uigilia. Sequendo

prout potuit intentioni ipsius a qua si defecit non malicie

sed ignorancie etc.   fol. 40

[The four preceding folios (now numbered 21-24),
also displaced, disarranged among themselves,
and partly illegible, seem to belong to this commentary.]

d) <Liber Petri de Alvernia> de motibus animalium.

Inc.: SIcut innuit philosophus in tercio phisicorum . . . fol. 40

Expl.: et hoc in uniuersali consequenter dicendum est

de generacione animalium.   fol. 46^V

[Unbracketed part of title added in marg. by later

hand, which also writes <u>explicit de motibus anima-lium</u> at end. Cf., e.g., <u>Thomae Aquinatis Commentaria</u>, ed. Junta (1551), fols. 46-57^V.]

<u>e</u>) <Liber Petri de Alvernia> de iuuentute et senectute.

Inc.: SIcut dicit philosophus primo phisicorum. Innata est . . .   fol. 46^V

Expl.: tunc accidit mors propter defectum infrigida-tionis.   fol. 57

[Unbracketed part of title added in marg. by later hand; and a third hand writes <u>Incipit septum</u>. Cf., e.g., ed. Junta, fols. 63-79^V, lect. I-XVI (misnum-bered XXVI).]

<u>f</u>) Incipit liber de morte et uita magistri petri de aluernia.

Inc.: Est quidem omnibus postquam philosophus de morte determinauit . . .   fol. 57

Expl.: in proporcionem habent ad mortem et vitam fere.:. Explicit sentencia magistri petri de aluernia de morte et vita.   fol. 61^V

[Title written on marg. in later hand; and a third hand adds <u>de morte et uita</u>. Cf., e.g., ed. Junta, fols. 79^V-82^V, lect. XVII (misnumbered XXVII)-XVIII.]

<u>g</u>) <Liber Guglielmi Hispalensis de> phis<i>onomia.

Inc.: SIcut dicit philosophus primo rethorice nobilitas est . . .   fol. 69^V

Expl.: ad astrorum scientiam transferat mentem suam.   fol. 80^V

[Unbracketed part of title written in marg. by another hand. Following text a table of contents in a contem-porary hand, which omits separate listing of item <u>f</u>, as well as the text on fol. 1^V (see general account below).]

xiv c., parchment, 80 fols. Main body of ms. (fols. 2-80) written in two, possibly three, similar hands: (1) fols. 2-34, double cols. 20.4 x 5.9 and 20.4 x 6.1 cms., 55 lines; (2) fols. 35-80, double cols. 20.5 x 6.3 cms., varying 55 and 58 lines (variations in ink may in-dicate third hand). Rubr. red and blue. Some marg. gloses, correc-tions, and titles. Present fol. 1^V, written in a hand similar to (1) and evidently of separate origin, contains a brief untitled text begin-

ning <u>Omnes homines natura scire desiderant circa librum istum</u>
<u>quedam in generali</u> . . . <u>queritur utrum in sciencia methaphisica.</u>
<u>sciendum sit ipse deus</u> . . . , and is followed (col. 2) by a figure of
five concentric circles. Damage has caused the loss of some folios
from original ms. and the disarrangement of others (xvii c. or
earlier), among which a number are also stained and partly illegible:
see nn. to items <u>a</u>-<u>c</u> above. On fol. 1^r, otherwise blank, a table of
contents in a modern hand.

311 (X. 129: Pieralisi I, 409-10; ñ.a. 768).

A miscellany, chiefly medical, of which the following texts are
in Latin:

<u>a</u>) <Kalendarium.>

Inc. text.: Januarius habet dies xxx. Nox habet oras xv

dies nouem . . .   fol. 1

[A calendar of church observances, in double cols.,
one for each month. Expl. fol. 3^v. Fol. 4 originally
blank.]

<u>b</u>) <Regimen sanitatis salernitanum.>

Inc.: Roberto Regi describit scola Salerni Si uis incolu-

men . . .   fol. 22^v

[See above, <u>MSS. 178</u>, item <u>e</u>, and <u>186</u>, item <u>d</u>; and
below, <u>MS. 3957</u>. Expl. fol. 24^v.]

<u>c</u>) Incipiunt nomina et Virtutes balneorum Puteoli et baya-

rum sicut in libro .x.^{o} oribasii uetustissimi medici

continetur ✔

Inc.: INter opes rerum. deus est Laudandus in illis . . .fol. 25
Expl.: Vt possint nati scribere e facta tui.   fol. 58^v

[Pietro da Eboli, <u>Carmen de balneis Puteolanis</u>; also
attributed to Alcadinus. Cf. Bibl. Angelica, <u>MS. 1474</u>,
in Giacosa, <u>Mag. salern.</u>, pp. 397-99.]

xv c., paper, 64 fols. Written in various hands: (1) fols. 1-3; (2) fols.
5-24; (3) fols. 25-58; (4) fols. 59-62; (5) fol. 64. In addition to items
above, contains five texts in Catalan: (1) fols. 5-14: Arnaldus de
Villanova, <u>Liber conservationis sanitatis</u>; (2) fols. 14-18^v, untitled
work beginning <S><u>egons que es acostumat e demostrat per los</u>
<u>sanis de medecina</u>; (3) fols. 19-22, untitled work beginning <Q><u>Vi</u>

vol ausir lo bon tractat; (4) fols. 59^V-62, tables for finding aureum numerum et festa mobilia beginning Si vols saber tot ço ques conte; and (5) an untitled work beginning En lo temps que los moros temen lo principat de Cathalunya. Item c has 33 full-page illustr. of text. Table of contents in modern hands on front fly leaf; and on fol. 4^V, in a modern hand, a note beginning Leo Decimus Summus Pontifex, nulla alia in re ardentius et effusius, quam ad liberalitatis gloriam anhelauit.

312 (X. 130: Pieralisi I, 411; n.a. 784 and VII.B.22).

a) <Magistri Theodorici de Cervia Practica cyrurgiae.>

Incipiunt capitula in libro cyrurgie episcopi de ceruia. fol. 1

Inc. prooem.: Tractaturi de uulneribus et cyrurgie scienciam tradituri . . .   fol. 2

> [Explicit on fol. 77. Present ms. listed in Thorndike and Kibre, col. 725; and Mieli, Gli scient. ital., I.2, 320. See Giacosa, Mag. salern., pp. 437-40; and M. Sarti and M. Fattorini, De claris archigymnasii bononiensis professoribus (2nd ed., Bologna, 1888-96), I, 537-44.]

b) <Ad dentes dealbandos.>

Inc.: Ad dentes dealbandos et mondificandos accipe malmor
album regulam rubeam pumicem . . .   fol. 77^V

Expl.: multum emundat et prohibet a putredine et
uermi.   fol. 77^V

> [Differs from various Salernitan recipes among the texts printed in S. De Renzi, Collectio salernitana (1852-59), and in Giacosa, Mag. salern., where the nearest parallel is in the Catholica on p. 106. Incipit not listed in Thorndike and Kibre, and not noted in Pieralisi.]

xv c., parchment, 81 fols. (numbered I-III and 1-78). Item a in double cols. 18 x 6.1 cms., 27 lines, and written in single hand. Item b added in another hand. Rubr. in blue and red. On fol. 2 an ornamental border and initial in blue, grey, red, and gold. On fol. 2, top margin, in a third hand: Practica: Magistri Theodorici de Ceruia. in cyrurgia peritissimi.

328 (X. 146: Pieralisi I, 438-41; n.a. 796 and VII.C.11.).

a) Incipit liber ypoc<r>atis pronosticationis vite et mortis

secundum motum lune per 12 signa et aspectum planetarum
quem transtulit Frater guiglelmus de morletta ordinis
fratrum predicatorum archiepiscopus de Corinto.

Inc.: Dixit ypocras qui fuit medicus et magister op-
timus . . .   fol. 2

[According to Thorndike, II, 924-25, this version varies
from those ascribed to Peter of Abano and William of
Moerbeke; but cf. Paris, Bibl. nat. MS. lat. 7337: Liber
hyppocratis . . . traductus a domino fratre Guglielmo
de Moerbecha archiepiscopo Corintino ordinis predicatorum. Expl. fol. 7^V. Present ms. not in Thorndike,
or Diels, I, 50.]

b) Incipit liber .4. tractatuum ptolomei al filii dhi [sic] in scientia iuditiorum astrorum <translatus per Platonem
Tiburtinum>.

Inc.: .i. Rerum Yesure in quibus est pronosticabilis . . . fol. 8

Expl.: in loco huic libro finem imponere Non incongruum
existimamus. + Explicit liber .4 quadripartiti.   fol. 70

[Cf., e.g., ed. Venice, 1519, fols. 1-94^V. See item e
below.]

c) + Incipit scientia proiectionis rad<i>orum.

Inc.: Cum proiectionem rad<i>orum stellarum. scire
volueris . . .   fol. 70

Expl.: erit laus Rad<i>ationis equate.   fol. 70

[An appendix to the Quadripartitum: Cf., e.g., ed. Venice,
1519, fols. 94^V-95; Björnbo, Bibl. math., 3, XII, 108; and
Carmody, Ar. astron., Pt. 43.]

d) <Incipit Liber> ptholemei de Judiciis partium et primo de
parte fortune . . .

Inc.: Quoniam In primo libro partium terminos . . .   fol. 70^V

Expl.: hiis duodecim mensibus mutatur.   fol. 76

[Title appears (fol. 70^V, top) as part of rubric +Ex-
plicit quadripartitus ptholomei de Judiciis partium etc.
Cf. Vat. MS. Pal. lat. 1892, fols. 99 ff.; and Carmody,
Ar. astron., Pt. 33.]

e) <Fragmentum libri primi Quadripartiti Ptholomaei e
translatione Platonis Tiburtini.> Capitulum X. in
fortitudinibus 4.^{or} temporum.

Inc. cap. X: Stellarum Itaque fortitudinem qualitatis . . . fol. 76^V

Expl. cap. XII: hyemalis. solstitii ordinati Succedentis. fol. 77^V

[Chaps. X-XII of item b above (cf. ed. Venice, 1519, fols. 14-15^V); but so displaced by original copyist: see items f and h below.]

f) <Fragmentum Centiloquii Hermetis. Liber translatus per Stephanum de Messana.>

Inc. sent. 92: Revelatur statim verbum occultum . . .   fol. 78

Expl.: numquam peccabis cum dei auxilio. Expliciunt flores diui hermeti trismegisti . . . hoc est flos florum.   fol. 78

[Sayings 92-100, as in ed. Venice, 1519, fol. 107^V, displaced from item h below.]

g) Capitula stellarum oblata Regi magno Saracenorum Bacham ab mansor [sic] astrologo filio . . . [?] Judei a platone tabularum [sic=tiburtino] translata.

Inc.: Signorum dispositio est ut dicam . . .   fol. 78

Expl.: in quo nulla fiet In Justitia + Completus est liber capitulorum mansori . . .   fol. 84

[=Iudicia Almansoris ascribed to Rasis. On fol. 78, marg., a modern hand writes Almansorii iudicia, seu Propositiones de Astris. Cf., e.g., ed. Venice, 1519, fols. 109^V-11; and Carmody, Ar. astron., 22.1a.

h) <Centiloqium Hermetis translatum per Stephanum de Messana.>

Inc.: Dixit Hermes quod sol et luna post deum . . .   fol. 84

Expl. sent. 91: quando aspiciuntur a sole tali signo.   fol. 87^V

[Ends with Saying 91; cf., e.g., ed. Venice, 1519, fols. 106^V-07^V. Sayings 92-100 have been displaced to item f above but by original scribe, since item i below continues on same fol. immediately following Saying 91. Note on fol. 87^V, marg. carta .5; and on fol. 84 a modern hand writes Liber Aphorismi centum Hermetis. See Carmody, Ar. astron., 7.3a.]

i) <Epistola Messahala de coniunctionibus planetarum translata per Johannem Hispalensem.>

Inc. prol.: Incipit Epistola mesahalla In rebus eclipsis lune . . .   fol. 87^V

Inc. cap. I: dixit messahallah quia dominus altissimus fecit terram . . .   fol. 88

Expl.: ex secretis scientie astrorum.   fol. 91^V

[= De rebus eclipsium. Cf., e.g., ed. Venice, 1519,
fols. 135^V-36^V, and Thorndike, in Osiris, XII (1956),
62 ff. See Carmody, Ar. astron., 1.7a, which erroneously lists MS. 303, fols. 83^V-87, for this item. On
fol. 87^V a modern hand writes Epistola Messallach
de Coniunctionibus planetarum.]

j) de significatione planetarum in domibus in primis de
   Saturno.

Inc.: Saturnus In oriente pro lege autem . . .   fol. 91^V

[Cf. Erfurt, MS. Amplon. Q. 372, fols. 50^V-54^V: De
significatione 7 planetarum in domibus Zergis
(= Jirgis, Girgith; Schum, Beschr. Verzeichniss, p.
623). See also Carmody, Ar. astron., 9.1.]

k) <Excerpta varia ex astrologis arabicis, e.g.:>
   [1] de stellarum lumine uel Radiis aomar <i.e. Omar>.

Inc.: Sed quoniam aspectus et huius . . .   fol. 95
   [2] de gaudiis stellarum zael.

Inc.: Amplius planetarum gaudium prout . . .   fol. 95^V

[Besides these two there are excerpts from Messahala, al-Kindi, Dorotheus, Albumasar, etc. For Omar
see MS. Amplon. 372, fols. 115-27^V: Omar de stellarum
lumine vel radiis; not in Thorndike and Kibre. Expl.
fol. 137.]

l) Incipit Centiloquium tolomei. <Fragmentum libri trans-
   lati per Johannem Hispalensem.>

Inc.: Iam scripsi tibi yesure . . .
   1. Sciencia stellarum ex te . . .   fol. 137^V

[Expl. fol. 142^V. Cf. Carmody, Ar. astron., Pt. 3b.
See below, item n.]

m) Tractatus de directionibus et de aspectibus et radiis. et
   de modis dirigendi et prohiciendi rad<i>os et aspectus.
   editus per magistrum matteum de guarimbertis de
   Parma archidiaconus [sic] parmensis.

Inc. prooem.: PEr aspectus radios planetarum . . .   fol. 143
Inc. cap. I: PRimo uideamus quid sit directio . . .   fol. 143^V
Expl.: clima quodcumque uoluimus: Postmodum quo docemur
   superius in quinto Capitulo; Explicit tractatus de directionibus et de aspectibus et Radiis et de modis dirigendi

et prohiciendi Rad<i>os et aspectus. Editum per magistrum
matteum de parma archidiachonum parmensem./   fol. 163

[Title and the words Explicit tractatus . . . parmensem
at end in another hand, which characteristically writes
"ct" ligatures like "tt." Fols. 163^V-64^V blank; on fols.
165-70^V Tabule directionum et aspectuum. Ms. listed in
Thorndike, III, 769.]

n) Centiloquium ptolomei cum comento haly.

Inc.: Mundanorum ad hoc et ad illum . . .   fol. 171

Expl.: Rogo te Igitur quod dignum etiam est Vt nemini

committas eum Istum nisi Illi qui Intelliget eum . . .

perfecta est huius libri translatio 3° die mensis martii

et duodecima die mensis Jumedi. 2^O anno arrabum. 300

+ Explicit Centiloquium ptholomei cum comento haly.
                                                fol. 194^V
[Cf. ed. Venice, 1519, fols. 97-106; and Björnbo, Bibl.
math., 3, XII, 103, and n.1.]

o) <Additio prima ad Centiloquium Ptholomaei.>

Inc.: Ptholomeus dixit quod stella cum caudis sunt

.9 . . .   fol. 195

Expl.: significat magnam mortalitatem et decollatio-

nem.   fol. 195^V

[= De cometis. Cf. Björnbo, Bibl. math., 3, XII, 103;
and Carmody, Ar. astron., Pt. 3d.]

p) <Additio altera ad Centiloquium Ptholomaei.>

Inc.: Cum Volueris scire cholorem eclipsis lune . . .   fol. 195^V

Expl.: In 3 facie eius ascendit vir nudus.   fol. 196^V

[Cf. Björnbo, Bibl. math., 3, XII, 103.]

q) Incipit liber haly de horis eligendis <translatus per

Platonem Tiburtinum et Savasordam>.

Inc.: Rogasti me karissime ut tibi librum . . .   fol. 197

[Cf. above, MS. 182, item c, and 256, item b, and below,
MS. 335, item a. Expl. fol. 236 with a group of tables.]

xv c., paper, 236 fols. (+ 110 blank leaves). Written in two hands:
(1) Fols. 2-142^V and 171-236, single cols., varying 28-32 lines.
(2) Fols. 143-70^V, double cols., varying 35-38 lines. Fols. numbered

1-236, but some given a second number in same hand, i.e. fols.
162, 163, 195, 196, 197, marked 20, 21, 25, 26, 27, respectively.
On fol. 1, marg., <u>Caroli Strozzę Thomę filii 1635.</u>

332 (X. 150: Pieralisi I, 445-46; n.a. 1713).

<u>a</u>) <Liber Guglielminae, i.e. Guglielmi Placentini de Saliceto
 Practica siue Summa conseruationis et curationis.>

<u>Inc. prol.</u>: EORVM AUTEM que fiunt et posse sciri et
 habent causas determinatas et ordines . . .   fol. 1

<u>Inc. cap. introd.</u>: In hoc omnes conueniunt sapientes
 cum medicus . . .   fol. 1^v

<u>Inc. lib. IV, pars 2</u>: que est de medicinis simplicibus
 requiritur in sui principio . . .   fol. 308

<u>Expl.</u>: oppilationes nutritiuorum lenit naturam ualet in
 scabie et febribus antiquis.   fol. 317

[Original first fol. of ms. missing, apparently without
loss to text proper. The work is named thus on fols.
178 and 241: <u>Incipit liber secundus Ghuiglielmine,</u>
<u>Incipit tabula 3^{11} libri Gughelmine</u>. But cf., e.g., <u>Guli-</u>
<u>elmus Placentinus de Saliceto, Summa conseruationis</u>
<u>et curationis</u> (Venice: [Johannes et Gregorius de Gre-
goriis], 8 May, 1490). Present text ends, incomplete,
in section of alphabetical list of simples, with sentence beginning <u>Fumus terre</u>, corresponding to
passage on sig. $^{S}1^v$, col. 2, of printed ed. Fols. 317^v–
25^v blank.]

<u>b</u>) Tractatus de uenenis secundum conciliatorem <id est
 Petrum de Abano>.

<u>Inc. prol.</u>: REuerendissimo in Christo patre et domino
 innocentio diuina prouidentia summo pontifici petrus
 de ebano minimus medicorum cum deuotione presens
 scriptum tam uestre petitioni . . .   fol. 326

<u>Inc. text.</u>: <Q>Via oppositum est cibo . . .   fol. 326

<u>Expl.</u>: Explicit tractatus breuis et utilis de uenenis secun-
 dum petrum de ebano alias dictum conciliatorem/ ebanum
 est castrum in comitatu Padue// conciliator fuit artis
 paduanus anno Christi M^{o}CCC^{o}X^o Amen deo gratias
 amen   fol. 337

[There follows a table of chapters. Dedication by Petrus
to a Pope Innocent seems impossible and may be errone-

ous scribal expansion of letter N. Giacosa, Magistri
salern., p. 495, notes dedications to John XXII and
Honorius IV, and the other Latin texts known to Thorndike, II, 935-36, cite the pope without name, as N, as
John, or as John XXII (an Italian transl., however, in
Venice— MS. S. Marco XI, 82—also names Innocent;
see Isis, XIII, 87, n. 89). For significance of date, plac-
ing Petrus as "conciliator" in Padua in 1310, see
Thorndike, II, 879-80. Ms. not in Sante Ferrari, pp.
141-42.]

xiv c., paper, 337 fols., single cols. 22 x 15.7 cms., 39 lines. Original fol. 1 missing and present leaves renumbered. Written in
single hand. Rubr. in red. On present fol. 1 in a modern hand vol.
1713.

333 (X. 151: Pieralisi I, 447; n.a. 1715).

a) <Mundini de Foro Iulii Sinonima abbreviata nominum
   medicinalium rerum quae diffuse olim Symon ianuen-
   sis tractaverat.>

Inc.: Qvoniam nichil karius et amicabilius antiquis fuit,
   quam breuissime loqui . . .   fol. 1

Expl.: pro ea zedoaria vtimur. Expliciunt synonima secundum Magistrum Mundinum de foroiulii natione. ciuitati
   padue legentie / deo gracias   fol. 67^V

[An abbreviation, with the addition of new words, made
by Mundinus Austria ciuitate diocesis aquilgenensis in
studio paduano anno M^{O}CCC^{O}XXI inductione quarta die
XI augusti (cf. Giacosa, Magistri salern., p. 503). For
the original work of Simon of Genoa see above, MS. 171,
item a.]

b) INCIPIT Antidotarium nicolay.

Inc.: AVrea ab auro dicta est alexandrina dicta est
   alexandrina ab alexandro . . .   fol. 68

Expl.: <Z>Inziber conditum sic fit . . . perficit, sanat.
   <De ponderibus.> Et quia sufficienter de dispensatione . . .
   amicorum plenitudine glorientur sit laus deo omnipotenti amen Explicit liber nicolay deo gratias amen.
                                                      fol. 84^V

[Lacks prologue but has final chap. on weights and
measures, as, e.g., in Mesue, Opera (ed. 1533), fols.
243-271^V. Cf. Choulant, Handbuch Bücherkunde, I
(Leipzig, 1841), 286-87; and Dorveaux, L'Antidotaire
Nicolas (Paris, 1896). See also Giacosa, Magistri

salern., pp. 375-78, 435, 441, and 496. Incipit varies
from Thorndike and Kibre, col. 72.]

xv c., paper, 85 fols., written in two hands: (1) Fols. 1-67^V, single
cols. 23.6 x 13.5 cms., 55 lines. Written with black ink in precise,
angular style. (2) Fols. 68-84^V, double cols. 22.5 x 7.3 cms., 41
lines. Written with lighter ink in a freer, less angular style. In
part (2) spaces are left for rubr. initials but none executed.

335 (X. 153: Pieralisi, 450; n.a. 795 and VII.C.12.).

a) Primum capitulum ali filii abrayi in electionibus horarum
    laudabilium. <Liber translatus per Platonem Tiburtinum
    et Savasordam.>

   Inc.: <I>n nomine domini. Dixit Ali filius acham ebram.
       Rogasti Karissime ut tibi librum de horis eligendis . . .
                                                       fol. 1
   Expl.: gradu et momento . . .   fol. 11^V

       [Cf. above, MS. 182, item c; MS. 256, item b; and
       MS. 328, item q.]

b) <Liber de geomantia.>

   Inc.: Istarum autem figurarum .8. sunt paris numeri.
       et 8. disparis numeri de quibus est figura una .8.
       punctorum 4^{or} figura singule sunt . . .   fol. 12
   Expl.: in juditio sit necessario. et probatur pro red'les
       quod est 14^a figura si est uis bona uel similiter. lauda-
       bilis Deus sit de religienti [?] suo.   fol. 61^V

       [Opening lines apparently missing.]

Originally two separate mss.: (1) Fols. 1-11, xiv c., parchment,
double cols. 23.3 x 7 cms., 44 lines. Written in similar hands of
three different sizes: fols. 1-2, fols. 2^V-6, and fols. 6^V-11^V. Rubr.
in red. (2) Fols. 12-64, xv c., paper, single cols. but with some
lists in double cols. Written in single hand. Opening initial, some
titles and figures rubr. in red. Tables illustrating text throughout.
Fols. 52-54 and 62 ruled, otherwise blank; fols. 63-64 blank. Front
fly leaf has table of contents in modern hand. On fol. 1, upper inside margin, the date 1454; and on fol. 12 the date 1459. On fol. 1,
lower margin: Caroli Strozzę Thomę filii 1635.

336 (X. 154: Pieralisi I, 451; n.a. 1936).

<Liber Almagesti Ptolomaei translatus per Gerardum Cremonensem cum additamentis e versione altera de Arabico commentisque e Campano Novariense.>

Inc. prol. pr. Gerardi: QUIDAM princeps nomine
Albuguase . . .   fol. 1

Inc. prol. alt. Gerardi: Liber hic precepto maymonis
Regis Arabum . . .   fol. 1^V

Inc. I, 1 Ger.: BOnum scire fuit quod sapientibus . . .   fol. 1^V

Expl.: honestum est ut ponamus hoc finem libri; Expleta
est dictio .13^a. libri ptolomej. Et cum eo completur
liber Almagesti De Disciplinalibus.   fol. 297

[Extracts from a second translation from the Arabic in
marg. but fewer and more fragmentary than in MS. 173
above (q.v.); e.g. alternate I, 1 and opening of bk. IV are
missing. Present ms. not in Haskins, Med. sci., pp. 105-
8. In addition text is heavily glosed in marg. (especially
through dictio 3^a, fol. 72) with extensive passages from
Campanus (many marked Campanus, Camp., or C): see,
e.g., fols. 15-21, 26-29, 33^V, 40-43. Tables follow text,
fols. 298^V-99, 300, 300^V, 302^V-5^V, 306^V. On verso of
unnumbered fol. preceding 1, in modern hand, Claudij
Ptolomaei Astronomia et ejusdem Almagesti liber.]

xv c., paper, 306 fols., double cols. 18.5 x 6 cms., 34 lines (varying). Text written in single hand; gloses in similar hand but with
browner ink. Fols. 297^V-98, 299^V, 301, 302, and 306 blank. Tables
and figures in text and marg. throughout. Rubr. red in text and
gloses.

340 (X. 158: Pieralisi I, 455-56).

A miscellany of tracts and quaestiones, of which five are
relevant to the present collection:

a) <Hervaei Natalis Tractatus de formis.>

Inc.: Ut ordinatius possint inueniri et per consequens ad
ea responderi . . .   fol. 1

Expl.: dispositiones accidentales carnis et ossis.   fol. 21^V

[Cf. Pelzer, Codd. vat. lat., II.1 (1931), 231; and Maier,
Codd. burghes. (1952), p. 359. Incipit not in Thorndike
and Kibre.]

b) <Hervaei Natalis Quaestiones de coelo sive de materia
coeli.>

Inc.: Queritur utrum aliqua uirtus actiua sit in natura

corporali . . .   fol. 22

Expl.: et sic respondetur . . . Hic Expliciunt Quaestiones

De Celo.   fol. 42

[Cf. Histoire litt. de France, XXXIV, 330-31; and
Hauréau, Schedario, s.v. Quaeritur utrum, etc., re-
ferring to ed. Venice, 1513.]

c) <Fragmentum notularum super spheram.>

Inc. (mutil.): que ex predeterminatis sunt manifeste. et

ultimo [?] infert ex hac differentia quodam correla-

tionum speciale de eclipsis . . .   fol. 44

Expl.: et totam mundanam machinam mundi superioris

dissolui. Expliciunt notule super speram.   fol. 51^V

[Cf. Sphere of Sacrobosco, ed. Thorndike, p. 117, but
text does not seem to coincide with any of the commentaries or glosulae in this ed.]

d) In nomine domini pii et misericordis. Incipit Liber Maioris

Introductorii Albumassar astrologi in scientiam Iudi-

ciorum astrorum. et in naturis. etc.

Inc.: Laus deo qui creauit celum et terram . . .   fol. 52

Expl. (mutil.): affinitas uero numeri est unde numeret

quadam pars alicuius numeri totum ex omni numero.

uerbi gratia. tres sunt   fol. 73^V

[The as yet inedited translation ascribed to John of
Spain; but for the question of identity of this translator
see Thorndike, II, 73 ff. Ends, incomplete, in Tractate
VI. See Carmody, Ar. astron., 13.1a.]

e) <Johannis de Gandavo Quaestiones super Librum Averrois

de substantia orbis.>

Inc.: Queritur utrum celum sit compositum ex duabus

naturis . . .   fol. 97

Expl.: Expliciunt questiones super de substantia orbis

disputate parisiis per magistrum iohannem de gend'. fol. 108^V

[Table of contents follows on same fol.]

xiv c., parchment, 108 fols. A miscellany written in at least 8 hands:
(1) Fols. 1-13^V, col. 1, double cols. 25.4 x 8.5 cms., 53-57 lines
(originally a gathering of 14 leaves, of which the first has been cut

away); and fols. 74-90^V, 25.4 x 8.4 cms., 52-56 lines, containing
quaestiones beginning Queritur vtrum in diuinis sit proprie verbum, Queritur vtrum actio manens in agente sic aliquid producere
effectiue, and Queritur vtrum beatitudo creature. (2) Fol. 13^V, cols.
1 and 2, double cols. 25.8 x 8.6 cms., 53 lines: contains a continuous fragment, partially erased, but with titles indicating contents:
Vtrum celum habeat naturam; Vtrum omnium corporalium sit una
natura; Vtrum lumen sit corpus; etc. A later hand at head of erased
section notes that the Tractatus de formis continues and is complete: Require precedens finem in sequenti folio quia continuatur
huic et nil deficit. (3) Fols. 14-21^V, double cols. 25.5 x 8.3 cms.
(some 28 x 8.4), 57-60 lines. (4) Fols. 22-43^V, double cols. 23.5 x
7.5 cms., 51-54 lines. Contains, besides item b above, an untitled
quaestio beginning (fol. 42) <P>rima ergo est vtrum naturali cog-
nitione possumus habere aliquam notitiam de deo . . . (5) Fols. 44-
51^V, double cols. 25.7 x 8.3 cms., 53 lines. (6) Fols. 52-73^V, double
cols. 25.8 x 8 cms., 67 lines. (7) Fols. 91-96^V, double cols. 26.4 x
7.4 cms., 57 lines, an untitled work beginning Simpliciores et minus
expertos confessores. de modo audiendi confessiones. (8) Fols. 97-
108^V, double cols. 25.4 x 7.3 cms., 59 lines. Rubr. of sections (1)-
(5) and (7) in red and blue, except fols. 86-90^V where rubr. is lacking. Rubr. of section (6) in red only. Section (8) is without rubr.
except for explicit on fol. 108^V. Vellum leaves of front binding contain fragments of a vocabularius, beginning Suffecit. subiecit. sup-
posuit . . . Thalami. cubicula maritorum, etc.; and of rear binding
fragments of a tract on justice and grace, beginning (mutil.): plus
tamen prestat Xristus regeneratis . . . Covers in brown leather
of Aragonese (?) origin, blind stamped with arms, as follows: three
palets quartered with a device having, in vertical thirds, four bars,
four fleurs-de-lis, and a cross-crosslet surrounded by four cross-
lets; the whole on a shield with fleurs-de-lis at right, left, and
bottom edges and surmounted by five additional fleurs-de-lis.

341 (X. 159: Pieralisi I, 457; n.a. 2313 and 1707).

Incipit liber compilationis phisionomie a magistro petro de padua
<seu de Abano> in ciuitate parisiensi.
Inc.: <N>obilitate generis Vrbanitatum titulus viro fulgen-

ti . . .   fol. 1

Expl.: hoc bonum optimum quoque creauit.   fol. 26

   [Ms. listed in Thorndike and Kibre, col. 431, and in
   Isis, XIII, 87 and n. 87. Not in Sante Ferrari, p. 143.]

xv c., paper, 26 fols., written in single hand. Ownership note on
fol. 1, lower marg.:Octauii Ferrarii. On inside front cover: Mano-
scritti che à S. Cm^a. Sa inuiato tra le robe dott. Villain L'Humani-
sta di Padova Signor Octauio Ferrari al Cmo. dal Setto che li
presenti à S. Cm^za.

343 (X. 161: Pieralisi I, 459-61).

A miscellany of prognostications and other scientific writings of
   various dates and from various sources, among which are the
   following relevant items:

a) Natiuitas.

   Inc. text. primae figurae: Currente anno Domini .1456.
        die 16 Nouembris. post meridiem hora .13. sm ho:
        existimatas Ad meridiem Bononii . . .   fol. 2

        [A series of figures with explanatory texts. Expl. fol.
        12^v. Not in Thorndike and Kibre, but see Thorndike,
        IV, 451, n. 52.]

b) Incipit Tractatus de Lapidibus et eorum coloribus quali-
        tatibus. et virtutibus per Alfabetum.

   Inc.: Adamas est lapis preciosus / obscurior cristal-
        lo . . .   fol. 33

   Expl.: Viperarius fit de linguis uiperarum . . . Sic lapis
        positus super sal . . . ualet contra Luxuriam/ Finis
        ad laudem Dei eiusque sanctissimae genetricis.   fol. 37^v

        [Varies from Thorndike and Kibre, col. 28: Adamas est
        durus cristallo obscurior. Cf. Saxl, Verzeichniss, II
        (1927), 103. Fols. 38-40 blank.]

c) <Petri de Monte Alcino Iudicium astrologicum in anno
        mccccxviii.>

   Inc. prol.: Sicut testatur Auroys [= Averroes] in perhenni<bu>s
        libri<s> de auditu naturali oportet sapientes esse bonos . . .
        et ideo ego petrus quondam bernardi de monte alcino timore
        domini ductus cupiens aliqua futura docere in anno m.cccc

18 que debent secundum naturam corporum supercelestium

euenire . . .   fol. 51

Inc. text.: Anno igitur .m.cccc xviii incompleta . . .   fol. 51

Expl.: per quam mereamur ad gloriam attingere sem-

piternam amen—   fol. 54

[On fol. 51, marg., another hand writes Petri de Monte
Alcino. Not in Thorndike and Kibre, but see Thorndike,
IV, 90.]

d) <Fratris Nicolai Guardentini [?] Iudicium astrologicum
in anno 1352.>

Inc.: Magnifice domine. Si quod uestra iussit mihi

nobilitas . . .   fol. 55

Expl.: Accipe igitur magne hoc opus exiguum. Breue

corpore/ uiribus amplum. A fratre nicolao Guētino

[-tirio, -cirio?] licet defectuose/ tamen fide sincera

discussum.   fol. 58^V

[Date of prognostication appears in text (fol. 1): anno
domini 1352 mense nouembris die 19. hora prima
completa diei. Not in Thorndike and Kibre, but cf.
Thorndike, III, 600 and n. 63.]

e) <Mauricii Centini> Manuale philosophicum.

Inc.: Philosophie uocabulum quod Pitagoras primus

agnoscit . . .   fol. 66

Expl.: in his inferiora corpora influxus.   fol. 80

[Ms. listed in Thorndike and Kibre, col. 487.]

xiv-xvii c., paper, 80 fols., composed of nine mss. or fragments in
varying sizes, written in nine hands at different dates, as follows:
(1) Fols. 1-12^V, xv c., containing item a. (2) Fols. 17-32, xvi c.,
containing a Liber secundus de generatione et corruptione. (3) Fols.
33-40, xv c., containing item b; fols. 38-40 blank. (4) Fols. 41-44,
xvii c., containing Libri tres disputationum; fols. 45-46 blank. (5)
Fols. 47-50, xvii c., containing Octogonum problema geometricum
authore Odoarde Farnesio Parme et Placentie duce. (6) Fols. 51-54,
xv c., containing item c. (7) Fols. 55-58, xiv c., containing item d.
(8) Fols. 60-64, xvii c., containing Dialogus de salubritate aeris
romani (listed in Isis, XIII, 93, sec. 91, but without indication of
date). (9) Fols. 66-80, xv c. (?), containing item e.

348 (X. 166: Pieralisi I, 465; n.a. 735).

Incipit liber per modum questionum magistri Johannis Versoris:
Super librum phisicorum Aristotilis.

Inc.: CIRCA INITIVM primi phisicorum queritur utrum de
rebus phisicis seu naturalibus sit scientia . . .   fol. 1

Expl.: que quidem causa est deus gloriosus / totius nature
gubernator et institutor. qui est in secula seculorum
benedictus. Finis Amen. Explicit liber questionum
super librum phisicorum Aristotelis Feliciter.   fol. 202

[A table of contents follows, fols. 202-4. See Thorndike and Kibre, col. 95 (but under Nicolaus Stoyczin
not Versor); and Suppl. II, p. 346, "Utrum scientia
naturalis sit circa . . . ."]

xv c., paper, 205 fols., double cols. 22.6 x 6.3 cms., 42 lines. Written in single hand. Rubr. in red and blue. Fols. 204^V-205^V ruled
but blank.

350 (X. 168: Pieralisi I, 467-68; n.a. 828 and VII.C.9.).

A collection of manuscript fragments containing eight texts, of
which seven are scientific writings:

a) <Perspectiva Rogeri Bacon.>

Inc.: <P>ropositis radicibus sapientie tam diuine quam
humane que . . .   fol. 2

Expl.: Vt animus moralis ignorans ueritatem. non posset
sustinere. explicit.   fol. 17

[Opus maius, pars V. A table follows text in another
hand. See Isis, XIII, 86, § 72. Not in Little, Roger
Bacon essays (1914), pp. 382-84.]

b) <Nicolai de Cusa> De Vna recti curuique mensura.

Inc.: Qvia vidi practicum magisterium commensura-
cionis curui . . .   fol. 20

[Cf., e.g., Opera (Basel, 1565), pp. 1101 ff. Expl.
fol. 23^V.]

c) Incipiunt canones <Azarchelis sive Al-Zarkali> in temporibus et motibus celi. <Translatio ascripta ad Gerardum
Cremonensem.>

Inc.: Quoniam cuiusque actionis quantitatem temporis
metitur spacium celestium motuum . . .   fol. 25

Expl.: Hec est machometh ad regem Persarum .9. ani et
.337. dies.   fol. 41^V

[See above, MS. 276, item a. Not in Boncompagni,
Gherardo Cremonese, pp. 57-58. Fol. 24 blank except
for title Canones in temp. et mot.]

d) De Mathematicis complementis Beatissimo pape Nicolao
Quinto Nicolaus Cardinalis sancti Petri ad vincula <id
est Nicolaus de Cusa>.

Inc.: Tanta est potestas summi tui pontificatus . . .   fol. 43
Expl.: que sunt mathematice complementa finit feliciter
brixine 1474. 24 nouembris.   fol. 60

[Cf., e.g., Opuscula varia (Strassburg, 1488 [?]). Ms.
listed in Thorndike and Kibre, col. 715, but undated.]

e) <Libellus de speculo mikesi magistri Johannis fontana
Veneti.>

Inc.: <C>um inferiorum cognitio ad celestium conducat
inquisitionem . . .   fol. 61
Expl.: Alio modo et commodosius Videtis.   fol. 65^V

[See Thorndike, IV, 175-76 and nn.; Abh. z. Gesch. d.
math. Wiss., XIV, 137; and Isis, XIII, 93, § 91, and
XVII, 34 ff. On fol. 61 another hand writes Libellus de
speculo mikesi magistri Johannis fontanta [sic] Venetus
N^O. VIII°.]

f) Tabula latitudinum .5. stellarum erraticharum.   fol. 77
Inc. text.: Si latitudinem trium superiorum inuenire uis.
scias . . .   fol. 77^V
Inc. secunda part.: 2^a particula que est de sinibus et de-
clinatione. <C>um cuiuslibet .ergo. scire uolueritis
sinum uel declinationem . . .   fol. 78^V
Inc. alia part.: De latitudine planetarum. Qvia alibi
sufficienter . . .   fol. 89

[A collection of tables, fols. 77 and 83-89, with explanatory
texts.]

g) Opus Nicolai Alamanni pro Equationibus .12. domorum celi
apud florentiam.   fol. 91
Inc. text.: Ad inuestigandum breuiter astrum et ceteros
domos celi. Scias gradum solis ad tempus . . .   fol. 92^V
Expl.: oppositos . . .   fol. 92^V

108

[A collection of tables, fols. 91-92, with explanatory texts. Ends incomplete with ending of ms. fragment. See Isis, XIII, 93; Thorndike, III, 601, and, for date (1464), IV, 440, n. 12.]

xiv and xv c., parchment and paper. A collection of ms. fragments from various sources as follows: (1) Fols. 1-20, parchment, xiv c. Written in two hands, one for text, one for table. (2) Fols. 20-24, paper, xv c. Written in single hand. (3) Fols. 25-42, parchment, xiv c. Written in single hand. (4) Fols. 43-60, paper, xv c. Written in two hands, fols. 43-50^V and 51-60, respectively; the second hand dated 1474 (see item d, Expl. above). (5) Fols. 61-65^V, paper, xv c. Written in single hand. (6) Fols. 72-76, paper, xv c. Written in single hand. Contains, fols. 72-73, Circa loycam reuerendi magistri alberti de Xaxonia [sic], omitted from the list of texts above. (7) Fols. 77-89, paper, xv c. Written in single hand. (8) Fols. 91-92, paper, xv c. At end of item a the back cover of the original binding of the ms. of which it is a fragment, is bound in with present collection. Present fol. 1 was added when this collection was made and contains table of contents in xvii-c. hand. On fol. 2: Caroli Strozzę Thomę filii 1635.

357 (X. 175: Pieralisi I, 475-81; n.a. 732).

a) <Blasii de Parma Tractatus de motu.>

  Inc.: In omni predicamento potest esse mutacio . . .   fol. 1
  Expl.: conferetur b igitur etc.   fol. 16^V

     [Present ms. noted in Maier, An der Grenze von
     Scholastik u. Naturwissensch. (Essen, 1943), p. 371,
     n. 2; and Divus Thomas 1946, II, 163, n. 5. See Thorn-
     dike, IV, 72 and 654; and Isis, XIII, 66, § 22.]

b) <Angeli de Fossombruno Quaestio de inductione formarum
     cum disputatione Bartholomei de Rido Patavini.>

  Inc.: Vtrum detur minima materia de cuius potentia possit
     per se forma aliquis . . .   fol. 16^V
  Expl.: posset forma induci quod sic non diceretur asinus
     cum quota none tali etc. 1416/ 24. septembris.   fol. 23

     [On fol. 18^V, col. 2, this statement: Et sic huius magni
     dubii finitur prima oppositio quam in disputatione ge-
     nerali ubi fuit magnorum doctorum congregatio proba-
     biliter substentaui Ego Bar. de Rido pactauus sub
     famoso artium doctore Magistro Angelo de fossanbruno
     huius questionis auctore pactaui quem tunc naturalem
     philosophiam legentem Anno a natiuitate cristi 1402. de

mense januarii quo pactaui tunc maxime studium libe-
ralium artium vigebat etc. Incipit listed under Angelus,
but not Bartholomeus, in Thorndike and Kibre, col. 753.]

c) <Johannis de Hollandia Tractatus de primo et ultimo instanti.

Inc.: Philosophus octauo phisicorum ponit aliquas

regulas . . .   fol. 23

Expl.: sed sufficit michi quod sint vtilia si sunt vtilia./ fol. 37^V

[Cf., e.g., Bodleian, Canon. misc. MS. 171, fols. 48^V ff.]

d) <Aegidi Romani et aliorum Quaestiones.>

Inc. pr. quaest.: Qvestio est utrum in celo sit materia uel

si celum sit corpus simplex . . .   fol. 38

Inc. quint. quaest.: Qveritur consequenter quinto utrum

necessario in qualibet generacione et corrupcione

. . .   fol. 48^V

Expl.: a pluribus agentibus non influentibus ad eius

productionem. Laus deo.   fol. 60^V

[On fols. 45-46 another quaestio interrupts, beginning
Vtrum possibile sit aliquam qualitatem intendi sim-
pliciter. On fol. 48^V the note: Explicit per me etc. 29
mensis maii 1469.]

e) <Perspectiva Blasii de Parma.>

Inc.: Primo queritur vtrum ad visionem causandam

necesse sit . . .   fol. 61

Expl.: Et sic est finis questionum scientie perspectiue

secundum excellentissimum arcium doctorem et astro-

nomorum sue etatis principem D. M. Blaxium de Pel-

lecanis de parma ad laudem et gloriam gloriosissimi et

eterni domini nostri ihesu cristi filii dei omnipotentis

et gloriosissime matris eius marie ac totius celicolarum

chori Amen. Laus deo.   fol. 107

[See Thorndike, IV, 658; Isis, XIII, 86, § 73; and Archeion,
IX, 187-88. On fols. 107^V-8 a table of contents ending:
Explicit . . . per me Theodericum gothalmanum 1469 vn-
decima die mens Julii. Deo gracias.]

f) <Johannis Peckham Perspectiva communis.>

Inc.: Inter phisice considerationis studia lux iocundius . . .

Lvcem aliquid operari in visum . . .   fol. 109

Expl.: per hoc quod in huius lapidibus contemplamur Et

sic est finis Amen. Deo gracias.   fol. 122^V

[Cf., e.g., ed. Cologne, 1592. A later hand notes incorrectly: <u>Blasii Parmensis opus.</u> On fol. 123 a table of contents. See Thorndike, IV, 658.]

xv c., paper, 126 fols., double cols. Written by Theodericus Gothalmanus in 1469 (see nn. to items <u>d</u> and <u>e</u> above). Fols. 123^V-26^V ruled but blank. Rubr. red and blue; and on fol. 1 a flowery border in red, blue, green, gold, etc., with coat of arms, unidentified. Notes of ownership: (fol. 1) <u>Codice acquisitato legitimamente da mio Zio Marchese Giambattista Costabili Containi in Roma nel 1835, ora ragalato da me, erede del sudetto mio Zio al Sig.^{r} Principe Barberini —Gio. Costabili, Firenze 9 Fbre 1851—</u>; (inside front cover) <u>Della Costabiliana di Ferrara—Rassegnato al Chiarissimo Sr Cav. Angelo Pezzana per cui il Gracioso Esame 13—1840 attendendo il retorno del Codice Codice No. 88.</u>

461 (XI. 104: Pieralisi II, 130; n.a. 2446).

<Alberti magni Summa naturalium seu Philosophia pauperum cum commento.>

<u>Inc. prol.</u>: Inuocata virgo maria etcetera.   fol. 1

<u>Inc. text.</u>: <P>hilosophia diuiditur in tr<es partes> scilicet in loycam . . .   fol. 3^V

<u>Expl. text.</u>: malum gracia desistente Etcetera Est finis summe naturalium alberti.   fol. 168^V

<u>Inc. comm.</u>: Circa huius tractatus inicium cuiusque uerba secundum ordinem sunt recitanda . . .   fol. 169

<u>Expl. comm.</u>: et edera fontes et bibe.   fol. 177

[For explicit of text (=bk. V), see Geyer, <u>Beiträge,</u> XXXV. 1, 13-14, esp. items 9-15, 18, 20, and 21; and the same pp. 46-54 <u>et passim</u> on question of ascription to Albertus de Orlamunda. Present ms. not in Grabmann, <u>Beiträge</u>, XX. 2, 29-46; Mandonnet, <u>Rév. néo-scol.</u>, XXXVI, 230-62; Birkenmajer, <u>Philos. Jahrb.</u>, XXXVII, 271 ff.; nor Geyer. Incipits of prologue and <u>commentum</u> not in <u>Gesamtk. d. Wiegendr.</u>, Grabmann, nor Thorndike and Kibre. Cf. below, MSS. <u>462</u> and <u>480</u>.]

xv c., paper, 177 fols. Written in single hand. On fol. 177^V: <u>frater Martinus Erestus</u> [?] <u>magister studentium</u> and <u>anno domini 1486 post omnium sanctorum incepi legere philosophiam naturalem pro gradu magisterii Studentium Restené.</u> Bound in red with Barberini bees on spine and Cardinal Barberini's coat of arms on covers.

462 (XI. 105: Pieralisi II, 131; n.a. 2447).

a) <Alberti magni Summa naturalium seu Philosophia pauperum.>

Inc.: Philosophia diuiditur in tres partes . . .   fol. 1

Inc. lib. V: <S>Icut dicit damasce<n>us impossibile est

aliquam substanciam . . .   fol. 107^V

Expl.: Est enim liberum arbitrium facilitas [sic] <rationis>
et voluntatis quia bonum eligitur gratia exeunte [sic] et
malum gratia desistente./ Etc Est finis Explicit quintus
et vltimus liber summorum naturalium magni Alberti
Et est finitus anno domini millesimo Quadricentessimo
vicessimo septimo feria quarta ante aduentum domini
per manus cuiusdam ffrancissci de De [sic] Queźua.//
Hoc iste scribebat qui primo scribere discebat =ffran-
cisscus scribebat margaretha sibi calamat' tenebat
etc   fol. 134

[On fol. 101^V is the colophon Explicit Albertus magnus
anno domini m^{o}cccc^o vicesimo septimo, followed by
blank leaves to 107, where a commentary on bk. V begins: Iste est liber quintus similiter naturalium alberti
in quo determinatur de anima . . . ; and on fol. 107^V the
text of the book itself. The commentary occupies fol.
107 entire, thereafter runs alternately in left- and right-
hand columns paralleling the text, and ends on fol. 134^V.
Bk. V is of the A Recension as in Beiträge, XXXV, 1,
38-62, ed. Geyer, who does not, however, list present
ms. Cf. above MS. 461 and below MS. 480.]

b) <Tractatus Avicennae de mineralibus translatus per
Alfredum Anglicum. Cum commento.>

Inc. comm.: Circa inicium huius libri videndum est de
tytulo et causis istius libri et Primo sciendum est
quod presens liber intitulatur tractatus auicenne de
mineralibus . . .   fol. 136

Inc. text.: <T>Erra pura lapis non fit quia continuum
non facit sed . . .   fol. 138

Expl. text.: medii caloris et similiter hoc tempus adiacet
motui Se/^{2} etc.   fol. 169^V

[Throughout commentary irregularly occupies entire
folios or surrounds the text, ending on fol. 169^V. Text
ed., e.g., in Theatrum chemicum, IV (Argentorati, 1659),
883-87. Cf. Baeumker, Sitzungsb. d. Bay. Akad., Phil.-
hist. Kl., 1913, 9^e Abh., pp. 26-27, n. 2; and Beiträge,
XVII, 5-6, 181-82.]

xv c., paper, 169 fols., single cols. but with some instances of double cols. where commentary parallels text. Texts written in single hand (cf. explicit to item a), commentaries in same or similar hand but smaller. Some gloses, marginal and interlinear. Bound like MS. 461 (q.v.).

473 (XI. 116: Pieralisi II, 148; n.a. 1762).

a) Incipit liber de proprie<tatibus> rerum Rabani.

Inc. prol.: CVm proprietates rerum sequuntur . . .   fol. 1

Inc. text.: De proprietatibus itaque et naturis rerum

. . .   fol. 1^V

Expl.: attrahendo venenum uipere sanare consueuit.

explicit liber xviii.   fol. 263^V

[Not Rabanus but Bartholomaeus Anglicus, and lacks bk. XIX, "De coloribus," etc. Missing letters of title torn away with part of top marg. of fol. 1; but title is written again at bottom in modern hand. See Isis, XIII, 62, item 15, which, however, misdates the ms. and gives erroneous folio numbering (see general account of ms., below).]

b) <Notulae de remediis variis contra dolores capitis,

etc.>   fols. 28^V- 33, marg.

E.g.: nota contra dolorem capitis uetustissimam

. . .   fol. 28^V

nota Pillule ad stomachum et ad capud et ad uisum

occulorum ℞ Calami aromatici cubebe . . .   fol. 29

Nota Contra lacrimas oculorum ℞ parum sal . . . fol. 31

[Items appear on fols. containing Bartholomaeus, bk. V "De capitis proprietate"; and on fol. 32 there is a note on text: Vertex est pars ea capitis qua capilli colliguntur . . . Not in Thorndike and Kibre, nor Isis, XIII, 62, item 15.]

c) Expositio uocabulorum obscurorum tractatus de spera.

Inc.: Dyametrum dicitur esse linea recta. transiens per

medium circuli . . .   fol. 89^V

Expl.: qui radii radiantur in nos. nisi esset in composi-

cio lune. Explicit.   fol. 89^V

[A note added in space following Bartholomaeus, bk. VII, and preceding bk. VIII, "De celo et mundo." Not in Thorndike and Kibre, nor Isis, XIII, 62, item 15.]

xiii c., parchment, 263 fols., double cols., main text (item a) written in various hands among which the parts were distributed. Rubr.
in red. Items b and c are added in two different xv-c. hands. On fol.
263^V still another hand writes a brief note beginning Intellectus in
fronte Memoria in cerebro Ira in felle Auaricia in iecore . . .

477 (XI. 120: Pieralisi II, 152-53; n.a. 84 and I.C.2.).

Described by Albers, Centralbl. f. Bibliotheksw., XX, 370-73. Cf.
Rév. bénédict., XX, 174-84; De Bruyne, Les anciennes trad. lat.
d. Machabées (1932), p. LIV; C. W. Jones, Bedae pseudepig.,
pp. 58 and 134, and (ed.) Opera de temporibus (1943), p. 167; and
Isis, XXVII, 435. The ms., x/xi c., is a miscellany in two parts,
containing the following relevant items: In part 1, fols. 72^V-110,
(a) Bede, De natura rerum, (b) Bede, De temporibus and (c) a
pseudo-Bede computus. In part 2, fol. 128^V, (d) a book list de
Galone qui Robertus uocabatur, which names a liber Aureus
de medicina. cum diuersis anthidotis and an Experimenta
diuersorum auctorum in vno uolumine.

480 (XI. 123: Pieralisi II, 157; n.a. 2445).

<Alberti magni Summa naturalium seu Philosophia pauperum cum
commento.>

Inc. prol. comm.: TVnc vnumquodque scientie arbitramur
 cum causas eius cognoscimus . . .   fol. 1
Inc. text.: Phylosophia Diuiditur In tres Partes scilicet
 logicam . . .   fol. 3

[Expl., incomplete, fol. 236^V. See refs. above, MS. 461,
none of which lists present ms. or incipit of present
commentum. Commentum not in Thorndike and Kibre.]

xv c., paper, 236 fols. Written in single hand, the text in single cols.
with commentary in smaller letters surrounding it. Rubr. red, with
initials in red, red and black, red and blue. Bound like MS. 461 (q.v.).

510 (XI. 153: Pieralisi II, 206; n.a. 52).

<Aurelius Augustinus De musica cum Retractatione (I.xi [x]).>
 Inc. Retract.: Sex libros de musica scripsi . . .   fol. 1
 Inc. lib. I: AVGVSTINVS. Modus qui pes est?   fol. 2^V
 Expl. lib. VI: hereticorum necessitate fecisse uideremus.
  Explicit Liber Sextus. .AVG. De Musica——   fol. 93

[Incipit of retractatio not in Thorndike and Kibre.]

xiii c., parchment, 93 fols., single cols. 16.8 x 11.8 cms., 25 lines. Written in single hand. Rubr. in red and yellow. On fol. 1, bottom marg. Cartusiae Villae nouae prope Avenionem. On fol. 2, bottom: Cartusień Vallis benedictionis. On fol. 93^V .i. florenis / Iste liber est Joui et vallis benedictionis emptus a domo due b̄o̅es.

531 (XI. 174: Pieralisi II, 233-34).

A collection of the works of St. Augustine, of which one is relevant to the present collection:
<De musica, lib. VI, cum Retractatione (I.xi [x]).>
Inc. Retract.: DEinde ut supra commemoraui .vi. libros
de musica scripsi . . .   fol. 70
Inc. lib. VI: Satis diu penes te . . .   fol. 70

[Cf. above, MS. 510. Expl. fol. 78^V.]

xiv c., parchment, 78 fols., double cols. 17.9 x 5.9 cms., 44 lines. Written in single hand. Rubr. in red and blue.

558 (XII. 1: Pieralisi II, 274; n.a. 1675).

<Isidori Hispalensis Etymologiarum sive Originum.>
Inc. epist.: Domino meo dei seruo Braulioni episcopo
ysidorus . . . Omni desiderio desideraui . . .   fol. 1
Inc. text.: Disciplina a discendo nomen accepit . . . fol. 1
Expl.: pro signo interdum pro cura adhibetur. ut uis morbi
ignis ardores siccetur. Laus tibi sit Christe explicit
liber iste. Explicit ethimologiarum ysidorus.   fol. 160

[Another hand writes, following explicit, the date 1338. Begins with Ep. I, and contains bks. I-XX. See MSS. 670 and 703 below.]

xiv c., parchment, 160 fols., single cols. 22.3 x 5.6 cms., 43 lines. Written in single hand. Rubr. in red.

33 (XIV. 6: Pieralisi III, 7; n.a. 72).

Iohannis presbiteri damasceni liber incipit in quo est traditio certa fidei ortodoxe capitulis diuisa .C. a burgundione iudice ciue pisano de greco in latinum domino Eugenio .III°. bone memorie pape translatus. Capitulum .1. Quomodo incompre- hensibilis deus et quomodo non oportet quererе . . . que non

sunt tradita nobis a sanctis prophetis et apostolis et euan-
gelistis. R⩚

Inc. : DEum nemo uidit unquam vnigenitus filius . . .   fol. 1

Expl.: cum angelis in uitam eternam cum domino nostro
    Ihesu Christo uidentes et uisi. et indeficiens id quod
    est gaudium fructificantes. Amen.   fol. 69^V

[In part (chaps. 15-45) treats cosmology and human
physiology and psychology. For title and mss. see, e.g.,
J. de Ghellinck, in Revue des quest. hist., LXXXVIII,
149-60, esp. pp. 158-60 and nn.; for the division into
100 chaps., p. 159, nn. 6 and 8 (cf. Migne, PG, XIV,
783-88, "Capita dogmatica"). See also Haskins, Med.
sci., p. 207, n. 83. Not in Thorndike and Kibre.]

xiv c., parchment, 69 fols., double cols. 18.8 x 5.9 cms., 36 lines.
Written in single hand. Rubr. red and blue.

666 (XIV. 39: Pieralisi III, 83; n.a. 236 and III.B.7).

<Thomae Cantipratarii Universale bonum de apibus.> INcipiunt
    capitula libri qui dicitur uniuersale bonum de apibus scilicet.
    de prelatis et subditis. In libro qui dicitur bonum uniuersale:
    Inter cetera loquitur actor ita dicens . . . Rex apum mellei
    coloris est ex electo flore . . .   fol. 1

Inc. dedic.: Reuerendo in Christo patri fratri huberto
    . . .   fol. 1^V

Inc. text.: UNum caput Christum . . .   fol. 2

Inc. al. cap.: Cenomanensis inclita ciuitas . . .   fol. 2^V

Expl.: Et rogo ut si aliquid in hoc labore uel aliis umquam
    meruerim illum tanquam me participem faciat. Ihesu
    dominus dominus noster qui cum patre et spiritu sancto
    uiuit et regnat deus. per omnia secula seculorum. Amen.
    Explicit. deo gracias. Amen.   fol. 123

[Contains the two books of the Universale bonum; see,
e.g., ed. Douai, 1597, esp. pp. 1, 2, 5, and 499. For
Cenomanensis inclita ciuitas as incipit see Thorndike
and Kibre, col. 91.]

xv c., parchment, 123 fols., double cols. 20 x 6.3 cms., 40 lines.
Written in single hand. Rubr. in red and blue. On fol. 1 a modern
hand writes: Thomas Cantipratarius.

670 (XIV. 43: Pieralisi III, 87; n.a. 2137).

<Isidori Hispalensis Etymologiarum sive Originum.> Capitula primi libri ysidori . . .

   Inc. epist.: Domino meo et dei servo. Bralioni episcopo.

     Isidorus . . . Omni desiderio desideraui . . .   fol. 1

   Inc. text.: Disciplina a discendo nomen accepit . . .   fol. 2

   Expl.: prosigno interdum pro cura adhibetur ut uis morbi ignis ardore siccetur. Explicit . . .   fol. 100

    [Epistle preceded on 2 unnumbered fols. by table of contents of bks. I-XX. See above, MS. 558, and below, MS. 703.]

xiii c., parchment, 102 fols (2 s.n. + 100), double cols. varying 24 x 7.2, 24 x 7.5, and 24.5 x 6.9 cms., 51-53 lines. Written in two contemporary and similar hands. On fol. 1 a third hand writes the title ysidorus ethimologiarum. On fol. 1, bottom margin: Caroli Strozzę Thomę filii.

676 (XIV. 49: Pieralisi III, 98; n.a. 738).

   a) <Alberti Magni Liber de vegetabilibus et plantis.> Incipit liber primus de Vegeta<bi>libus cuius primus tractatus est an planta uel non Capitulum primum et est digressio declarans modum et ordinem et materiam huius libri.

     Inc.: In uniuersalibus principiis uiuorum . . .   fol. 1

     Expl.: Explicit liber vegetabilium.   fol. 117^V

    [See Opera omnia, ed. Borgnet, X, 1-305.]

   b) Incipit liber de nutrimento et nutrito eiusdem alberti. Primus tractatus est de nutrimento et nutrito per se. Capitulum quid sit libri intencio et quid est nutrimentum.

     Inc.: De anima secundum seipsam in precedenti libro dictum est . . .   fol. 117^V

     Expl.: Similiter autem mus/ et vermes multum ponunt in semine. Hec igitur de nutrimento et nutrito secundum suum diuersum esse secundum peripateticos dicta sint a nobis.   fol. 124

    [See Opera omnia, ed. Borgnet, IX, 323-41.]

xv c., parchment, 124 fols., single cols. 19 x 12.9 cms., 44 lines. Written in single hand. Rubr. in red and blue. Elaborate illuminated initial, on fol. 1, in red, green, blue, yellow, and gold.

677 (XIV. 50: Pieralisi III, 99; n.a. 76 and I.B.7).

A collection of works chiefly by Lactantius, of which three are
relevant to the present catalogue:

<u>a</u>) Lactantii Firmiani de opificio hominis Liber Incipit.

Inc.: Quam minime sim quietus. summis etiam neces-
sitatibus . . .   fol. 152

Expl.: Lactantii firmiani de opificio hominis liber explicit.
die Martis .VII°. Julii 1433. in Bononia.   fol. 164

[See the references in ed. Brandt-Laubmann (Corp.
script. eccles. lat.), XIX, xiii ff., and XXVII, vii ff.,
which do not, however, list present ms. Incipit not in
Thorndike and Kibre. Cf. above, <u>MS. 42</u>, item <u>a</u>.]

<u>b</u>) Lactantii firmiani iucundissimum ac lepidissimum carmen
de ortu obituque phoenicis incipit. lege feliciter.

Inc.: Est locus in primo foelix oriente remotus . . .   fol. 164^{V}

Expl.: Eternam vitam mortis adepta bono— Finis.   fol. 166^{V}

[In title the word is <u>laepidissimum</u>, with <u>a</u> cancelled
by a dot. Following title a later hand adds in lighter
ink: <u>inuentum Basileae</u> (cf., e.g., ed. Cratander, 1521).
For mss. and eds. see items in ed. Brandt-Laubmann,
XXVII, xviii ff.; Schanz-Hosius-Krüger, <u>Gesch. d. röm.
Lit</u>. (3rd ed., 1922), VIII.3, 433; and ed. Fitzpatrick (Diss.,
Philadelphia, 1933), p. 8; but none of these lists present
ms.]

<u>c</u>) Incipit phenix secundum claudianum.

Inc.: Occeani summo circumfluus equore lucus . . .   fol. 167

Expl.: In te dira legunt. nec uis habuere nocendi Finis.   fol. 168

[After title the same later hand as that in the note to
item <u>b</u> adds: <u>Inuenta papie</u>. Present ms. unknown to
Jeep, who examined other Barberini mss. of Claudianus: ed. Jeep (Leipzig, 1876), I, xxx ff., esp. 1-li.]

xv c., 1 fol. parchment, 168 fols. paper; fols. 2-169 single cols., the
prose texts 19.2 x 13.1 cms., 37 lines. Written in single hand. Fol. 1,
in another hand, partly faded and illegible, added from another source
and containing (1) Testimonia to Lactantius and (1^{V}) the title: <u>Lactantii
Firmiani Institutionum contra Paganos Liber Primus Incipit de Falsis
Religionibus quas Copiosa Oratione Refellit. et Vanas Esse Beneme-
rito Comprobat. Lege Feliciter</u>. Fol. 169 ruled but blank. Opening
initials of the Lactantius pieces elaborately illuminated in red, blue,
green, yellow, and gold. Ms. contains, besides items listed above:

(1) Fols. 2-138, <u>Lactantii Institutiones</u>; (2) fols. 138^V-51^V, <u>Lactantii</u>
<u>Ira dei</u>. On fol. 138, margin, following the explicit of item (1): <u>die</u>
<u>25 Junii 1433 Bononia</u>/ (see explicit of item <u>a</u> above).

703 (XIV. 76: Pieralisi III, 150; n.a. 1674).

Incipit liber ethimologiarum ysidori yspalensis. episcopi.

   <u>Inc. epist.</u>: Domino meo et dei servo Brauiloni . . .   fol. 1

   <u>Inc. text.</u>: Disciplina a discendo nomen accepit . . .   fol. 1

   <u>Expl.</u>: pro signo interdum pro cura adhibetur. uis morbi
      ardore succetur [<u>sic</u>!]. Explicit .XXIIII^{or}. [<u>sic</u>!] liber
      ethymologiarum ysidori yspalensis.   fol. 192

     [There follows another <u>epistola</u>: Inc.: <u>Domine meo ac</u>
     <u>dei seruo braulioni episcopo ysidorus</u> . . . ; Expl.: <u>sicut</u>
     <u>extat conscriptum stilo maiorum</u>. See <u>Ep</u>. VI, ed. Lindsay.
     For the address of this letter to Braulio, instead of
     Sisebutus, see <u>MSS HTU</u>, ed. Lindsay, nn. <u>ad loc</u>. Cf.
     <u>MSS 558</u> and <u>670</u> above.]

xiv c., parchment, 192 + 1 fols., double cols. 22.3 x 7 cms., 43 lines.
Written in single hand. Rubr. in red and blue, and initials for each
book elaborately illuminated with ecclesiastical figures and borders
of flowers, animals, and <u>putti</u> in red, blue, purple-grey, and gold. On
fol. 192^V and unnumbered leaf following, accounts in Italian in another
hand; and on verso of unnumbered leaf: <u>paulo de mosio militi f.</u> Fragment of homily bound in as front fly leaf: Inc.: <u>detrahetur et deroga-</u>
<u>bitur posteriori vltime voluntat</u> . . . <u>vt possibile sit habeant</u> . . . ;
Expl.: <u>Et tunc quia huiusmodi disposiciones non</u> . . .

27 (XXII. 44: Pieralisi IV, 410; n.a. 734 and VII.A.4.).

Three works by Dominicus de Dominicis Venetus, of which one is
   relevant to the present collection:
Tractatus de sensibus interioribus domini dominici episcopi
   brixiensis olim torcellani Sacre theologie et artium magistri.
   Incipit theologie et artium magistri. Incipit liber de sensibus
   Interioribus . . . secundum opynionem domini alberti magni/
   <u>Inc.</u>: QVedam de sensibus interioribus in presenti opusculo
   . . .   fol. 1
   <u>Expl.</u>: Explicit liber de virtutibus seu sensibus interioribus
      editus a venerabili artium doctore d. dominico de domini-
      cis veneto 1436 iuxta paduam dum ibi logicam legeret.

Deo laus Amen. fol. 8^V

[An unprinted (?) treatise of Dominicus de Dominicis:
this and other works in present ms. not in Gesamtkat.
d. Wegendr., s.n.; nor Guarnaschelli and Valenziani
Indice, I, 164; etc. For the author see Fabricius, Bibl.
lat. med. et inf. aet. (ed. 1858), II, 647; Agostini, Scritt.
viniziani, I (1752), 386; Valentinelli, Bibl. mss. S. Marci,
II, 225, and VI, 103; MS. Vat. lat. 1057; Trithemius; and
Gesner. Not in Thorndike and Kibre.]

xv c., paper, 100 fols., double cols. 21.3 x 6.3 (some 6.5) cms. Written in single hand. Rubr. red and blue. Fols. 11-69: expositio . . .
Super librum perierminyas aristotilis. Fols. 71-99^V: expositio . . .
Super librum diuisionum boetii. On fols. 99^V-100^V is a Summa libri,
followed by a list of 5 quaestiones.

1667 (XXIX. 11: Pieralisi VI, 11; n.a. 3396).

<Milonis Poema de mundi philosophia.> Incipit prologus in libro
de mundi philosophia.

Inc.: Mens celer armatur doctrinas [sic = doctrinis] philosophorum . . . fol. 1

Expl.: asserit ut ueterum sententia philosophorum. fol. 9

[On fols. 4^V-7 and 8^V-9^V there are cosmological figures similar to those in the text of Milo found, for
example, in Douai MS. 749, fols. 93^V ff. Present ms.
unknown to Delisle, Bibl. de l'École de Chartes, XXX
(1869), 323 ff.; and to Vernet, Bernardus Silvestris
et sa "Cosmographia", Appendix (unpubl. diss., École
de Chartes, 1936), which establishes a text based on
Douai MS. 749, British Museum MS. Add. 35112, and
Tours Bibl. mun. MS. 789: see Bibl. de l'École de
Chartes, XCVIII (1937), 191. See also Raby, Hist. sec.
lat. poetry, II, 14.]

xiv c., parchment, 9 fols., single cols. 10.4 x 5.7 cms., 27 lines.
Written in single, tiny hand. Rubr. in red. Originally formed fols.
120-28 of the ms. numbered 3396; present fols. 1 and 2 have old
fol. numbers 120 and 121, crossed out. Some gloses in a later
medieval hand. Ms. evidently of French origin; on fol. 2, outside
margin, a xvii-c. hand writes: Monsigneur [?] Voyam la commodite
passee entre hommes e femmes.

1771 (XXIX. 115: Pieralisi VI, 127; n.a. 1477, XVI.B.25, and k.xlix).

Alani <de Insulis> ANTICLAVDIANVS.

Inc.: Murice terra nouum contendit pingere celum . . .   fol. 1

Expl.: Susplantare nouas saltem post fata silebit.

Finito libro sit laux [sic] et gloria Christo. Explicit
anti liber Claudiani Alani.   fol. 56

[Begins, incomplete, at i.3, l. 9; cf. Migne, PL, CCX,
490A, and ed. R. Bossuat (Paris, 1955), p. 59, l. 63.
Does not have additional verses at end entitled A Deo
semper incipiendum et in Eundem desinendum: Migne,
CCX, 575-76. See De Lage, Alain de Lille, p. 185, and
ed. Bossuat, pp. 14 ff. Incipit not listed in Thorndike
and Kibre.]

xiii c., parchment, 56 fols., single cols. 15.5 x 6 cms. (some irregu-
lar variations in width), 36 lines. Written in single hand. Initials
rubr. in red on first six fols. only, but spaces left throughout for
further rubr. Some gloses, marginal and interlinear, in another
hand. Ownership notes: on inner back cover, Iste liber est falchonis
domini Nichole olim domini falchonis de hag^ano qui manet astolas
magister municipalis [?] designatus; same place in another hand,
Questei libri e di lapo di Ser dino da petrognano de la corte di
Simifonte; same place in a third hand, di Martinuccio figliuolo di
tolandino da Sangimig<nano>; same place in a fourth hand, di
cionellino da sangimignano de dare ala compagnia. On fol. 1: Caroli
Strozzę Thomę filii 1635. Bound in vellum with old library number
k.xlix on front cover. Ms. and binding both imperfect, with losses at
top and outer margins through fol. 41. On fol. 1 a later hand writes:
deest fol.

906 (XXIX, 250: Pieralisi VI, 356-57; n.a. 2390).

Incipit <Alani de Insulis> liber anteclaudiani de cunctis scientiis
et de perfecto homine.

Inc.: AVtoris mendico stilum phalerasque poete . . .   fol. 1

Expl.: Supplantare nouas saltem post fata silebit. amen.

Explicit liber anticlaudiani de cunctis scientiis uel de
beato puero uel homine. Deo Gratias Amen. amen. amen
amen amen.   fol. 58^v

[Contains nine prefatory verses:
AVtoris mendico stilum. phalerasque poete.
Ne mea segnitie clio deiecta senescat.
Ne iaceat calamus scabra rubigine torpens.
Scribendi nouitate / uetus iuuenescere carta /
Laudet. et antiquas cupiens exire latebras /

121

Ridet. et in tenui iuuescit arundine musa.
Fonte tuo sic phebe tuum profunde poetam /
Vt compluta tuo mens arida flumine. germen
Donet. et in factum concludat germinis usum.
Cf. Migne, PL, CCX, 487-88, and ed. R. Bossuat
(Paris, 1955), p. 57. Does not have additional verses
at end entitled A Deo semper incipiendum etc.: Migne,
CCX, 575-76. See De Lage, Alain de Lille, p. 185; and
above, MS. 1771. Incipit not listed in Thorndike and
Kibre.]

xiv c., parchment, 58 fols., single cols. 16.8 x 8.6 cms., 38 lines.
Written in single hand. Rubr. in yellow and red. Note on fly leaf:
Anticlaudiani liber de cunctis scientiis et de perfecto homine.
accedit praefatio .9. versuum quę non extat in editis. Ownership
notes: on fly leaf (different hand from previous note), Ricordanza
come a di 8. di Maggio 1425 dono Ser Giuliano prete della chiesa
di san piero buono consiglo di Firenze questo libro a domenico
figliuolo di Francesco di Pagliolo Mattei da Cetingnano, il quale
libro vole che per suo amore dentro studi; and on fol. 1 (new hand),
Caroli Strozzę Thomę filii. Bound in half vellum on boards with
coat of arms (three bars sinister on an almond-shaped device
within an almond-shaped border) in black ink on back cover.

1952 (XXX. 25: Pieralisi VII, 38-42; n.a. 2709).

A miscellany of fragments from various sources containing the
   following Latin scientific texts:

a) <Tractatus Claudiani Mamerti de statu animae cum Epistola
       Fausti Reiensis.> Tractatus que uisibilia et inuisibilia
       sint contra quem tribus libris qui sequuntur Claudianus
       iste disputat copiose subtiliter et argute. Non est autem
       Claudianus poeta sed alius ad quem Sidonius scribit. et
       de hoc libro facit celebrem mentionem . . .

   Inc.: PRecipis ut respondeam que in rebus humanis . . . fol. 1

       [Begins, as regularly with Claudianus mss., in midst
       of Faustus' letter: see ed. Engelbrecht (Corpus script.
       eccles., Vienna, 1885), p. 8, ll. 15-16 and n. 15, and
       p. 3, n.   Expl. on fol. 55. Present ms. not in ed. Engel-
       brecht (see pp. i-viii, and 2). Listed in Thorndike and
       Kibre, col. 504, from Vat. MS. lat. 989, under heading
       Claudianus, Que visibilia et invisibilia sint.]

b) <Andreae de Sommario Tractatus de astrorum motu.>
   Inc.: <M>Otus stellarum an sit scibilis nescio . . .   fol. 55^V

Expl.: reliqui scienciam uilipendunt.   fol. 67^V

[This is Andreas' work known also as De stellis et motu earum and Quod astrologia non possit sciri. See Pelzer, Codd. vat. lat., II.1 (1931), 465, s. cod. 989, no. 3.]

c) <Johannis de Legnano Tractatus de cometa.>

Inc.: <Q>Via sicut Ptolomeus in centiloquio uerbo quinto
ex iudiciis astrologicis . . .   fol. 68

Expl.: triumphantis uiuendo perducat.   fol. 78

[On the comet of 1368. Present ms. not in ed. Thorndike, Latin treatises on comets (Chicago, 1950).]

d) Incipit liber beati ysodori [sic] qui dicitur imago mundi.

Inc. prol.: <A>d instructionem multorum quibus deest copia
librorum Editum hic libellus cui nomen est ymago mundi
quia totus quasi in speculo . . .   fol. 142^V

Inc. text.: Mundus igitur dicitur quasi vndique motus
. . .   fol. 142^V

Expl.: Abides est insula in despontum in europpa hec
sita est contra . . .   fol. 145

[= Honorius Augustodunensis [?], De imago mundi. Ends, incomplete, in I, 34 (Migne, PL, CLXXII, 131).]

e) <Fratris Boccadi Theotonici Descriptio terrae sanctae.>

Inc.: <C>Vm in veteribus ystoriis legamus sicut dicit
beatus iheronimus quodam lustrasse . . .   fol. 146

Expl.: Explicit liber de descriptione terre sancte editus
a fratre boccado theotonico ordinis fratrum predicato-
rum.   fol. 169^V

[Not in Thorndike and Kibre. There follows a poem of six verses, beginning: Anna solet dici tres concepisse marias.]

f) <M. Tulli Ciceronis Somnium Scipionis.>

Inc.: Cum in affricam venissem a mallio consule . . .   fol. 183

[A brief fragment of the opening lines, ending on fol. 184.]

xv c., paper, 202 fols. A collection of ms. fragments in various hands: (1) fols. 1-78, (2) fols. 79-96, (3) fols. 97-120, (4) fols. 121-69, (5) fols. 170-77, (6) fols. 178-82, (7) fols. 183-84, (8) fols. 185-

87, and (9) fols. 188-202. Titles of items b, c, and e written by
other hands than those of their texts: b, De astrorum motu; c, De
cometis; e, Descriptio terrę Santę. It should be observed that the
order and contents of fragment (1) parallel those of MS. Vat. lat.
989, items 1-4; see Pelzer, Codd. vat. lat., II.1, 464-65. In addition
to the items listed above, the following works, not of scientific
interest, occur: Fols. 79-120^V—Poggio, De nobilitate; Poggio, Ep.
ad Gregorium Corarium; Carmen de nobilitate Caroli Aretini ad
Poggium; Ad Leonellum Estensem et Ludovicum de Gonzaga adu-
lescentes illustres Luciani de amicitia; Lucianus, De amicitia;
Pauli Vegerii . . . ad . . . Imolae Dominum Ludovicum Alidosium
pro dejecta Virgilii statua in Karolum Malatestam invectiva; Vita
Pauli Aemilii. Fols. 121-42—Anonymi descriptio Italiae (chiefly
historical). Fols. 170-82^V—A series of ancient inscriptions and
a funeral oration for Ludovic Cardinal of Aquileia. Fols. 184^V-202^V
—Carmen elegiacum ad Mapheum Vegium; Declamatio Colucii
Pierii Cancellarii Florentini; historical notes; Bonacursius Pistoi-
ensis, De nobilitate; Epistolae; Epistola Petri Pauli Vergerii; Oratio
Francisci Salimbeni, 1444; Epistole quattuor de matrimonio; five
short poems on classical subjects in Latin and Italian.

2089 (XXX. 162; Pieralisi VII, 321-22; n.a. 1479 and XVII.A.2).

A collection of the opera of Gregory of Mons Sacer, of which one
is relevant to the present collection:
Gregorij Abbatis Montis sacri Poema των αντρωπον θεοποίησεως
.i. De hominum Edificatione. Est autem Expositio mystica
septem dierum Creationis mundi.
Inc. epist. dedic.: In nomine Sancte et Indiuidue Trinitatis.
Incipit Epistola Dompni Gregorii Abbatis Montis sacri
quam destinauit Domino Magistro thome Sancte Sauine
Venerabili presbitero Cardinali. Super Libro quem
edidit. et eius nomini Dedicauit. Domino sancto . . . fol. 1
Inc. lib. I: Gregorii Abbatis Montis Sacri peri ton Antropon
theopiisis Liber primus Incipit. De celi et terre lucis
primarie creatione. et de die primo et eorum Significatis. Ducor ad alta noui perprima crepundia mundi
    . . .   fol. 2

Expl. lib. I: Diluuii retro semet sub uespere mersit',' Explicit
  liber primus de die prima .G. abbatis Montis sacri peri
  ton Antrophos theopijsis.   fol. 21
Inc. lib. II: Liber Secundus incipit de die secundo de firma-
  mento. et aquarum diuisione et eorum significatis. Uno
  mane die post uespere . . .   fol. 21
Expl. lib. II: Accipit elata dispersa uespere turri. Explicit
  liber secundus de die secundo .G. abbatis Montis sacri
  Peri. thon Anthropon. theopijsis.   fol. 40
Inc. lib. III: Liber tertius incipit De die tertio. de aquis.
  in mare congregatis. de diuersitatibus aquarum. de
  lignis et herbis fructiferis et sementiferis et eorum
  significatis. Iamque secunda suos exegerat ordine
  cursus . . .   fol. 40
Inc. lib. IV: . . . Tres sine sole dies . . .   fol. 58
Inc. lib. V: . . . Ordinibus distincta suis . . .   fol. 76
Inc. lib. VI: . . . CVm bene uel digne cessissent prime
  sequentes . . .   fol. 93^V
Inc. lib. VII: Liber Septimus incipit. de die septima. et
  de paradiso et eius cultura. et eorum significatis fi-
  guris. Septima tum post mane dies feliciter ortum . . .fol. 111^V
Expl. lib. VII: cui sit honor / uirtus / sit laus. sit gloria
  semper. AMEN. Explicit liber septimus de die septima.
  Deo Gratias.   fol. 131^V

[Title is written in two xvii-c. hands on a blank leaf
preceding fol. 1. An elaborate and continuous commentary in several similar and contemporary hands
accompanies text of poem throughout, dealing with
cosmological and other scientific matters suggested
by the poem. Of the epist. dedic. Pieralisi (VII, 321)
writes: "Ex hoc epistola ad Thomam Cardinalem S.
Sabinae, qui ab Innocento .iii. (1198-1216) creatus
fuit et ex duorum Cardinalium recordatione, idest
Petri S. Georgii ad Vellum Aureum, et Rogeri tituli
S. Anastasiae, quos magistros auctor audivit, eiusdem
auctoris aetas eruitur, de quo nec Tritemias, nec
Sixtus Senensis, nec Gesnerius verba faciunt. Haec
epistola in fol. p⁰." Both author and work are also unknown to Raby, A History of Christian-Latin Poetry
(2nd ed., 1953), and A Hist. of Secular Lat. Poetry
(1934); and evidently to the other modern historians
of medieval literature.]

125

xiii c., parchment, [1]+139 fols., single cols. 20.7 x 6 cms., 48
lines. Poem written in single hand, and same hand has written some
parts of the commentary. Following the Sacra poema are (fol. 132)
Oratio specialiter ad personam filij edita a dompno Gregorio Abbate,
(fol. 133) Flores psalmorum, (fol. 137^V) Sequentia in assumcione
gloriose virginis Marie, (fol. 137^V) In sanctis quorum reliquijs
habemus. Rubr. in red throughout.

2611 (XXXIII. 131: Pieralisi IX, 359-60; n.a. 874 and VIII.B.7).

<Gervasii Tilberiensis Otia imperialia sive Descriptio historica
totius mundi ab eius principio.>

Inc. dedic.: Ottoni quarto Romano Imperatori semper Augusto
Geruasius tilleberiensis uestri Signatione marescalcus
Regii . . .   fol. 1

Inc. text.: Duo sunt Imperator Auguste quibus hic mundus
regitur . . .   fol. 1

Expl.: Ad sinistram montis syon est ager peregrinorum
alchidemach secus viam que ducit / Explicit liber
iste.   fol. 208^V

[Ends, incomplete, in II^a dec., cap. xxii, "De situ terrae
sanctae secundum Theodosius," hence lacks the mira-
bilia cuiusque provinciae; cf. G. Leibnitz, Script. rer.
brunsvic., I (Hanover, 1707), 954. A table of contents
follows, through fol. 210^V, together with the rubr.:
Exitus operis epistola ad magistrum Johannem marcum
secretarium domini imperatoris, but the epistola itself
does not seem to occur. For ms. see J. Stevenson,
Chronicon anglicanum (Rolls Series, LXVI, London,
1875), "Preface," p. xxv and n. 2; and F. Liebermann
and R. Pauli, Ex rer. angl. script. saec. xii et xiii
(Mon. Germ. hist., SS., tom. XXVII, Hanover, 1885),
p. 362, no. 7. Cf. Pelzer, Codd. vat. lat., II.1, s. codd.
933 and 993. Incipit not listed in Thorndike and Kibre.]

xiv c., paper, 210 fols., single cols. 19.4 x 13.5 cms., 28 lines.
Written in single hand. Rubr. in red. Title, partly erroneous, in
modern hand on fly leaf: Descriptio historica totius mundi ad eius
principio. et de mirabilibus cuiusque Prouinciae. Auctore Geruasio
Tilleberiensi. On fol. 208^V, lower margin, in another hand: Conuen-
tus Sancte Marie Nouelle de Florentia. Or^{is} P. Apparently the same
inscription in same hand on fol. 1, top, but most of it missing with
the destruction of the margin.

2687 (XXXIV. 4: Pieralisi X, 9-10; n.a. 810 and X.2).

A collection of books of travel and geography, of which these are relevant to the present catalogue:

a) Incipit Itinerarium fratris Ricculdi.

Inc.: DVm ego minimus in ordine predicatorum recogitarem in compressitatem et intensionem . . .　　　fol. 1

[Ricoldus (or Richardus) de Monte crucis, Florentinus? See Fabricius, Bibl. lat. med. et inf. aet. (ed. 1858), I, 391; Trithemius; and Gesner. Expl. fol. 12^V. Not in Thorndike and Kibre.]

b) Incipit tractatus diuisionis et ambitus orbis terrarum et primo de paradiso delitiarum.

Inc.: Circa istam distinctionem queruntur duo primum utrum paradisus terrestris sit locus . . .　　　fol. 12^V

[Expl. fol. 30^V. Not in Thorndike and Kibre.]

c) Incipit liber de morum et gentium uarietatibus editus a Marcho Polo Veneto.

Inc.: Varietates morum et operationum et uirtutum gentium diuersarum habitantium . . .　　　fol. 37

Expl.: quod uix potest ibi uiuere homo uel animal. Esplicit libellus editus a domino Marcho Polo de Venetiis de diuersis prouinciis et gentibus mundi et de earum ritibus et moribus diuersis et actibus.　　　fol. 48^V

[A text of the Latin version LA, different to those made by Pipino and the anonymous translators from the Venetian. See Marco Polo, Il milione, ed. L. F. Benedetto (Firenze, 1928), p. cxix and n. 1, and pp. cv ff.]

xv c., parchment, 48 fols., single cols. varying in size, 42-52 lines. Written in single hand. Rubr. in red. On fol. 37, beneath title of c, another hand has written: Marcus polo; and the explicit is written twice by different hands. Fols. 30^V-37 contain a Libellus de mirabilibus vrbis Rome, beginning Mvrus urbis rome habet turres . . .

3957 (XLV. 51: Pieralisi XIV, 139; n.a. 223).

A miscellany of three works, of which one is a scientific piece in Latin:

Breuiarium <anonymi metrice compositum> ad conseruandum

127

corpus ab omnibus humoribus corruptis quod sequitur
teneat regimen et longhum tempus sanissime uiuet.

Inc. primus titulus: QQuisque compositus est ex quatuor
humoribus et primus est san\<g>uis . . .   fol. 159^V

Inc. pr. series versuum: Larghus amans ilaris ridens
rubeique coloris Cantans carnosus satis audax atque
benignus . . .

Inc. secundus tit.: Secundus humor est collera flaua
amara . . .

Inc. sec. ser. vers.: Hyrsutus fallax irascens prodighus
audax . . .

Inc. tertius tit.: Tercius humor est collera nigra . . .

Inc. tert. ser. vers.: Hic sonolentus piger in sputamine
multo . . .

Inc. quartus tit.: Quartus humor est flegma alba . . .

Inc. quart. ser. vers.: Liuidus et tristis cupidus nigrique
coloris . . .   fol. 159^V

[A series of topics arranged according to the four humors,
each stated in a metrical quatrain, and the whole occupying a single page. Based on the Regimen sanitatis salerni-
tanum; see, e.g., ed. Barbensi (Florence, 1947), pp. 22-23.
In present text the titles of the third and fourth topics are
evidently interchanged incorrectly. See also Thorndike
and Kibre, col. 383; and above, MSS. 178, item e, 186,
item d, and 311, item b.]

xv c., paper, 162 fols., written in three hands: (1) Fols. 1-158, a
Liber abaci in Italian beginning: Avendomi tu o soletto chiesto che
io componesse qualche operetta per lla quale che allabacho. (2) Fol.
159^V, the Brevarium, as above. (3) Fols. 160-62, Sallust, De bello
catilinario. On fol. 162^V, notes in Italian dated 1489 and 1490. On
parchment fly leaf at end (numbered 163), a figure and notes in
Italian on time-reckoning for dates running from 1482 to 1537.

INDEXES

GENERAL INDEX

Reference is regularly by manuscript and item. The following abbreviations occur: ascr. = ascribed to; comm. = commentary (by); gen. (after a number) = general account of ms.; note (after a number) = note to item listed; tr. = translator, translated by; vers. = version (of, by); Intr IIA = section IIA of the Introduction.

Abaci, liber, 3957 gen.
Abenahar
   Temp. pluv., 303 m
Abraham Judeo (see Savasorda)
Abredele, 296 a note
Abrelliele, 296 a note
Adelard of Bath
   Euclid, Geom., tr., 103
Aegidius Romanus, 309
   Quaest., 357 d
Aegidius de Thebaldis
   Haly, Jud. astror., tr., 172 a
Aesculapius, 160 (1)
Aesculapii Liber, 160 (9)
Aethicus Ister
   Cosmogr., 45
Alamannus, Nicolaus
   Equat. 12 dom. celi, 350 g
Alanus de Insulis
   Anticlaud., 1771, 1906
Albertus Magnus, 182 f (4)
   Comm., Philos. paup., bk. V,
     462 a note
   Nutrim. et nutrito, 676 b
   Philos. paup., 462 a; with comm.,
     461, 480
   Veg. et plantis, 676 a
Albertus de Orlamunda, 461 note
Albertus de Saxonia
   Circa loycam, 350 gen.
Albertus de Zacariis (Zancariis)
   Cautel. medic., 216 b

Albohali
   Nativ., 303 h
Albumasar, 182 h, 303 e note, 328 k note
   Conjunct. magn., 236 e (1)
   Conjunct. planet., 236 e (2)
   Flores, 236 e (1), 303 f
   Maior. introd., tr. John of Spain,
     340 d
   Sadam, 256 a
Alcabitius, 236 e (1)
   Isagog., tr. John of Spain, 236 b
Alcadinus, 311 c note
Alcantarus Caldeorum, 283 c note
Aldobrandini
   Libro della fisica, Intr IIA
Alexander Trallianus
   De puls. et urin., 160 (14)
   Therapeut., XI, 160 (10)
Alfonsinae, Tabulae planet., 296 a
Alfonsus, rex, 268
Alfraganus, 236 e (1)
   Diff. scient. astror., 303 b note;
     tr. John of Spain, 236 c
Alfredus Anglicus
   Avicenna, Mineral., tr., 462 b
Alidosius, Ludovicus, 1952 gen.
Alkindi, 171 e
   Epist. de aer. et pluv., 256 c
   Gradibus, 216 k
Almagest, versio alt., 173 and note
Almansor
   Capitula, tr. Plato of Tivoli, 328 g

INDEX OF INITIA